Beginner's Guide to Domestic Plumbing

Beginner's Guides are available on the following subjects:

Audio
Colour Television
Domestic Plumbing
Electric Wiring
Electronics
Integrated Circuits
Radio
Television
Transistors

Beginner's Guide to Domestic Plumbing

Ernest Hall
F.R.S.H.

Newnes Technical Books

The Butterworth Group

United Kingdom	**Butterworth & Co (Publishers) Ltd** London: 88 Kingsway, WC2B 6AB
Australia	**Butterworths Pty Ltd** Sydney: 586 Pacific Highway, Chatswood, NSW 2067 Also at Melbourne, Brisbane, Adelaide and Perth
Canada	**Butterworth & Co (Canada) Ltd** Toronto: 2265 Midland Avenue, Scarborough, Ontario, M1P 4S1
New Zealand	**Butterworths of New Zealand Ltd** Wellington: 26—28 Waring Taylor Street, 1
South Africa	**Butterworth & Co (South Africa) (Pty) Ltd** Durban: 152—154 Gale Street
USA	**Butterworth (Publishers) Inc** Boston: 19 Cummings Park, Woburn, Mass. 01801

First published 1977 by Newnes Technical Books
A Butterworth imprint

© Butterworth & Co. (Publishers) Ltd, 1977

ISBN 0 408 00283 2

Typeset by Butterworths Litho Preparation
Department

Printed by Chapel River Press, Andover, Hants.

Preface

A carpenter or bricklayer, miraculously transported from the early nineteen hundreds to the present day, would find the skills that he had acquired during his long apprenticeship no less useful in the late twentieth century. He would be delighted with the new power tools and equipment available to him, with the simplified cavity wall and cladding construction of modern times and (no doubt) with present day rates of pay and service conditions. Basically though, the materials with which he would be working and the way in which they would be used would be much the same as they were three quarters of a century ago.

A plumber, similarly transported, would find himself in a new and alien world. His skill in handling the traditional plumbing materials of lead and zinc would still be required: there are many thousands of British homes with plumbing installations that date back to before World War I. He would however find that most of his work involved the use of materials either unknown or unused in plumbing work at the turn of the century—copper, stainless steel and a wide variety of plastics.

He would find too that the modern plumber is no longer simply a 'skilled artisan' but a designer with a knowledge of physics and chemistry and something of the expertise of the engineer and the architect. Old rule-of-thumb installation methods have been discarded. Modern materials have made the plumber's physical tasks easier but modern design has immeasurably increased his responsibility. This is particularly true in the field of domestic drainage, where designs which thirty years ago would have been regarded as heretical—if not downright dangerous—are now in universal use. Their efficiency and safety depend entirely upon the installer's knowledge of the principles involved and the care with which he uses this knowledge.

This book does not claim to describe—much less to teach—*all* the plumber's skills. It is intended primarily for the householder who would like to be thoroughly familiar with the hot and cold water systems and the drainage system of his home. It will enable him to identify faults, to discuss intelligently plumbing repairs, alterations and extensions with his builder and, if he is a d.i.y. enthusiast, to carry out minor plumbing projects competently and safely.

I hope too that it may be of value to other workers in the building trade and to local and central government officials who, while not plumbers themselves, need to be thoroughly familiar with modern plumbing design and practice. Finally I hope, with some diffidence, that it may provide useful background reading to plumbing apprentices, particularly in the early stages of their careers. To these, and others, I would emphasise that words and illustrations cannot replace observation and practice. It is easy to describe the technique of making a wiped soldered joint. It is much less easy to put this technique into practice.

The householder, having read the appropriate chapters in the book, should trace *his* rising main from the Water Authority's stop-cock to the cold water storage cistern, should check that *his* hot water system is designed and installed in accordance with the principles described, should check the efficiency of *his* flushing cistern and the layout of the drains of his *home*.

Modern plumbing installation demands a thorough knowledge of theory and an acquaintance with the practical problems and difficulties likely to be encountered in any particular situation. I hope that something of both are to be found in this *Beginner's Guide*.

E.H.

Contents

1 Cold Water Services

Prior to the reorganisation of local government that took place on 1 April 1974, the responsibility for the provision of water supplies rested either with the local Borough or District Council or with one of the many statutory water under-takings. Since that date all-purpose Regional Water Authorities have been responsible for water supply, sewerage and sewage disposal. In many areas however the former water authority continues to act in that capacity as agent for the regional authority.

Water is distributed from the Authority's reservoirs by means of underground water mains, usually of iron suitably protected against corrosion. A branch communication pipe connects the main to a Water Authority stop-cock at the boundary of each property (*Figure 1.1*). It is at this stop-cock that the householder's responsibility for his water services begins.

The stop-cock will be found in a purpose-made pit, 3ft or more deep, with a hinged metal cover (*Figure 1.2*). Unlike the stop-cocks within the house, this one will probably have, instead of the conventional crutch or wheel head, a specially designed shank that can be turned only by means of one of the Authority's turn-keys. This enables water supply to be turned off when the house is unoccupied, or in the event of the occupier failing to pay his water rate!

From this stop-cock a service pipe (usually 15mm or ½in in diameter) is taken to within the house curtilage. This pipe should rise slightly throughout its length to permit any air bubbles to escape but, as a frost precaution, must be kept at least 0.82 metres (2ft 6in) below ground level.

The material of which the pipe is made will depend largely upon the date of its installation. Prior to the mid-1930s it would certainly have been of lead. Nowadays it is more likely to be of dead-soft temper copper tubing or even of polythene.

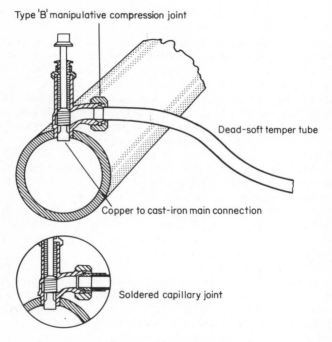

Fig. 1.1. Connection of communication pipe to main

Where the service pipe passes under the foundations of the house it should be threaded through lengths of drain pipe to protect it from possible damage as a result of settlement. The service pipe usually enters the house through the kitchen floor. Where this is of hollow boarded construction special

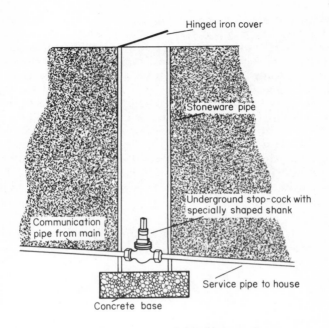

Hinged iron cover

Stoneware pipe

Underground stop-cock with
specially shaped shank

Communication
pipe from main

Service pipe to house

Concrete base

Fig. 1.2. The water authority's stop-cock

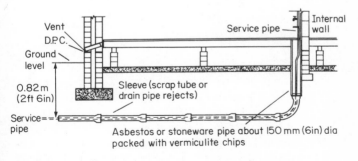

Vent

D.P.C.

Ground
level

Service pipe

Internal
wall

0.82 m
(2ft 6in)

Sleeve (scrap tube or
drain pipe rejects)

Service=
pipe

Asbestos or stoneware pipe about 150 mm (6in) dia
packed with vermiculite chips

Fig. 1.3. Service pipe entry under suspended floor

precautions must be taken to protect the pipe from exposure to the icy draughts that may whistle through the underfloor space. An effective method of protection is to thread the pipe through the middle of a 150mm (6in) drain pipe and to pack it round with vermiculite chips or some other similar inorganic lagging material (*Figure 1.3*). From the point at which the service pipe enters the house it is often referred to as the 'rising main'. In a modern home it is likely to be of half-hard temper copper tubing, though stainless steel or p.v.c. tubing may also be used.

Immediately above floor level the rising main should be provided with a stop-cock—the householder's main stop-cock. Immediately above this should be a drain cock (*Figure 1.4*).

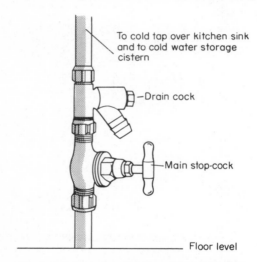

To cold tap over kitchen sink and to cold water storage cistern

—Drain cock

—Main stop-cock

Floor level

Fig. 1.4. Stop-cock and drain cock as rising main enters house

These two fittings permit the water supply to the house to be cut off and the entire length of the rising main drained when required.

In the past it was quite usual for all cold water services, including the bathroom cold taps and the w.c. flushing cistern, to be connected direct to the rising main. Today however, the regulations of most Water Authorities, and good plumbing practice, permit, at the most, four connections to this pipe.

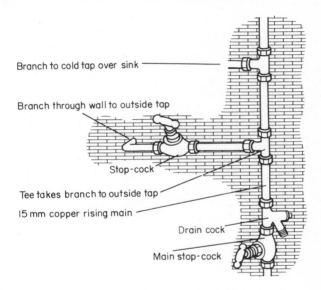

Branch to cold tap over sink

Branch through wall to outside tap

Stop-cock

Tee takes branch to outside tap

15 mm copper rising main

Drain cock

Main stop-cock

Fig. 1.5. Mains supply to outside tap

The first of these is to the cold tap over the kitchen sink. This is the tap that supplies water for drinking and cooking purposes and it is essential, on health grounds, that it should be supplied direct from the main and not from a storage cistern. A second connection *may* be made to the rising main at about the same level as the branch supplying the kitchen sink. This is for a branch supply pipe to serve a garden or garage tap (*Figure 1.5*). Such a tap can be provided only with the permission of the Water Authority who will usually make an extra charge on the water rate for its installation and use.

Typically, a garden supply pipe is taken through an external wall and turned over into a wall-plate elbow. A bib-tap, preferably fitted with a hose connector, is screwed into the outlet of this elbow. It is important that a separate stop-cock should be inserted into a garden supply branch pipe of this kind. At the onset of winter the stop-cock can be closed

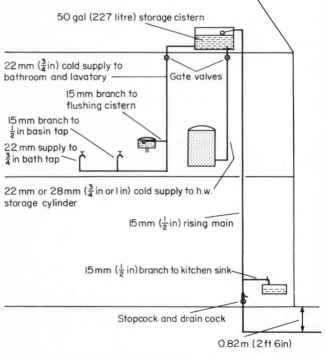

Fig. 1.6. Domestic cold water services

without affecting the other household services. The supply pipe can then be drained and the garden tap left open to eliminate the risk of frost damage.

From the kitchen the rising main will pass upwards to supply, via a ball or float valve, the main cold water storage cistern. This will probably be situated in the roof space. In its journey to the roof space the rising main should preferably be fixed to an *internal* wall though, in a modern home with central heating and cavity wall infilling, this is less important as a frost precaution than it formerly was.

The fourth, and final, branch that may be taken from the rising main of a well-designed modern plumbing system is also taken from within the roof space. It is to the ball valve supplying the small feed and expansion tank of an indirect hot water system, possibly used in conjunction with a central heating installation.

All other cold water services should be supplied by means of distribution pipes taken from the cold water storage cistern (*Figure 1.6*). There will usually be at least two, possibly more, of these. They should connect to the storage cistern at a level about 2in above its base to reduce the risk of grit and detritus from the water main being drawn into the distribution pipes.

Where there is a cylinder storage hot water system (whether direct or indirect) a supply pipe at least 22mm (¾in) and preferably 28mm (1in) in diameter must be taken from the cistern to connect to the cold supply tapping near to the base of the cylinder. Where the hot water system is a conventional indirect one (see Chapter 3) a drain cock should be provided in this supply pipe near to the cylinder connection to enable the cylinder to be drained.

It is very important that no branch supply pipe to any other draw-off point should be taken from the pipe serving the hot water storage cylinder.

Another cold water distribution pipe—again, at least 22mm (¾in) in diameter—is taken from the cold water storage cistern to provide bathroom cold water supplies. This is taken direct to the ¾in cold tap of the bath and 15mm (½in) branches are teed off it to supply the w.c. flushing cistern and the cold tap over the bathroom wash basin.

If an independent shower or a 'through rim' bidet are installed, separate 15mm (½in) cold water distribution pipes must be taken, direct from the storage cistern, to supply them with cold water. The reasons why *separate* supplies must be taken to these fittings will be explained when their installation is considered.

It is obviously to advantage to be able to isolate individual distribution pipes (to renew tap or ball-valve washers for instance) without affecting the rest of the household water supply system. This can be done by fitting gate valves into the distribution pipes close to the storage cistern. Make sure that these are the right size for the particular pipe-line (a 22mm gate valve for a 22mm distribution pipe) and that, when not in use, they are left *fully* open. A pipe is only as wide as its narrowest point! Alternatively each individual draw-off point can be isolated for servicing by fitting a small isolating stop-cock in its supply pipe just before connection to the tap or ball-valve concerned.

Stop-cocks and gate valves

The purpose of both stop-cocks and gate valves is to control the flow of water through water supply pipes. A screw-down stop-cock resembles in every way a conventional bib-tap set in a run of pipe. Turning the crutch or wheel head raises or lowers a washered valve or jumper onto a valve seating (*Figure 1.7*).

By far the commonest defect to which screw-down stop-cocks are prone is that of jamming in position after long periods of disuse. A sudden emergency such as a burst pipe or leaking cold water storage cistern sends the householder hurrying to the main stop-cock, only to find that it is immovable. A jammed stop-cock can usually be freed after applying penetrating oil and attempting to turn it, perhaps over a period of several days. It is however far better to stop it from jamming. This can be done by opening and shutting it several times, about twice a year. Every householder should make sure that all members of his family know where the main stop-cock is and that turning it off should be the first course of action in practically any plumbing emergency.

Stop-cocks, like taps, may occasionally need rewashering. To do this the water supply to the stop-cock must first be cut off. With the main stop-cock this will mean seeking the assistance of the Water Authority. The headgear of the stop-cock

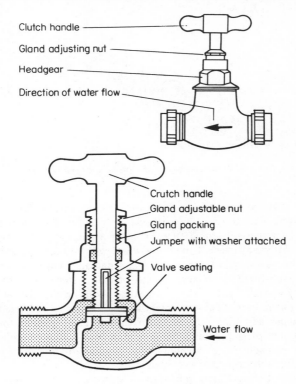

Fig. 1.7. Screw-down stop-cock

is then unscrewed and removed (*Figure 1.8*), the small nut holding the washer in place on the valve removed and a new washer—of the right size—fitted.

Failure of the gland packing is a rather more common defect. It will make itself known by water dripping from the stop-cock spindle. This demands immediate attention. A constant drip onto a wooden floor—particularly in the badly ventilated situations in which stop-cocks are often situated—can be the prelude to dry rot.

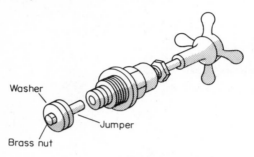

Fig. 1.8. Stop-cock headgear with jumper and washer

It may be possible to stop the drip by giving the gland adjusting nut—the first nut through which the spindle of the stop-cock passes—half a turn or so in a clockwise direction. Eventually however all the adjustment will be taken up and it will be necessary to renew the gland packing. Turn the stop-cock off—there is no need to cut off the water supply to it. Unscrew and remove the grub screw holding the crutch or wheel head in place and remove the head. Unscrew and remove the gland adjusting nut. Pick out the old gland packing with the point of a penknife blade and repack using household wool steeped in petroleum jelly. Caulk down hard. Reassemble the stop-cock and open it.

When fitting a new screw-down stop-cock make sure that it is fitted so that the arrow engraved on the stop-cock's body points in the direction of the flow of water. If it is fitted the wrong way round water pressure will force the valve down onto its seating and it will remain permanently closed.

Gate-valves closely resemble stop-cocks in external appearance but, when screwed down, a metal plate or 'gate'

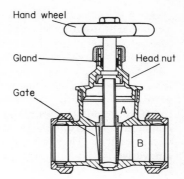

Hand wheel

Gland — Head nut

Gate

A

B

Fig. 1.9. Screw-down gate valve

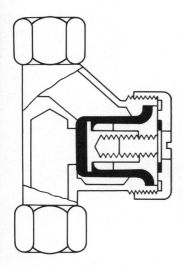

Fig. 1.10. Mini-stop-cocks for isolating taps or ball valves; upper, the Markfram; lower, the Ballofix

Connects to water supply pipe

Connects to tail of tap or ball valve

closes the waterway (*Figure 1.9*). Screw-down stop-cocks
are normally used in pipe-lines subject to mains pressure and
gate valves in situations, such as in the distribution pipes from
a cold water storage cistern, where the water pressure is low.

Isolating stop-cocks are small, unobtrusive control valves
that can be fitted into a pipe-line at any point to isolate a
particular tap or ball valve when required (*Figure 1.10*). They
therefore permit tap washering or renewal with the absolute
minimum of disruption to the remainder of the domestic
water services. They are opened or closed by means of a
screwdriver.

Drain cocks

A drain cock should be fitted at the lowest possible point on
any pipe that cannot be drained from a tap—immediately
above the main stop-cock, at the base of the cold water
supply pipe to an indirect cylinder or to a direct cylinder
heated by an immersion heater only, on the return pipe,
beside the boiler, of a hot water or central heating system.

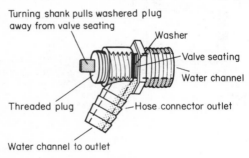

Fig. 1.11. A drain cock

The drain cock is opened by turning, with a spanner, the
square shank protruding from the body of the fitting
(*Figure 1.11*). This unscrews a washered plug from a valve
seating and allows the pipe to be drained. Drain cocks have a

hose connector outlet to permit drainage to an external gully. Drain cock outlets may become blocked with grit and the products of corrosion. They should therefore be opened, with a bucket placed underneath them, from time to time, to make sure that they are still working properly. If, when a drain cock is opened, water fails to flow, probing with a piece of wire will usually clear the obstruction.

2 The Cold Water Storage Cistern

The cold water storage cistern can be regarded as the 'heart' of the domestic hot and cold water services. Usually situated out of sight it should never be out of mind. It deserves regular inspection and maintenance.

Failure to fill properly can result, at the worst, in failure of all the domestic plumbing appliances. At the best it can result in intermittent supplies of water and recurring airlocks. A leak or overflow at a time when the family is away from home can result in hundreds of pounds worth of damage to carpets and furnishings.

Householders not infrequently query the necessity for the very existence of this potentially dangerous piece of equipment. They point out that it is technically possible to supply all cold water draw-off points direct from the rising main and that there are nowadays water heaters capable of providing a whole-house hot water supply that are designed for mains connection. Nevertheless the provision of a substantial cold water storage cistern offers real advantages both to the Water Authority and to the householder.

Demand for water is not constant throughout the day. There is a peak period of demand between 7.00 a.m. and 9.00 a.m. that few Water Authorities would be capable of meeting if all connections were made to the main. The cold water storage cistern provides a 'shock absorber' against peak period demand. At 7.00 a.m. all domestic storage cisterns are full. As the demand for water increases water pressure falls in the mains. Stored water is drawn off from storage cisterns which refill slowly during the peak period and more quickly as it passes.

From the householder's point of view a major advantage is that it makes possible (by providing a supply of water under constant, relatively low, pressure) the installation of that most versatile means of domestic hot water supply, the cylinder storage system. The fact that water in the distribution pipes is at low pressure from a storage cistern reduces the possibility of leaks and, if they occur, makes them less devastating. A low pressure supply to w.c. flushing cisterns helps to reduce the noise of refilling. Above all though, the provision of a substantial water storage cistern means that temporary failure of the mains water supply does not immediately paralyse the domestic plumbing system. All householders receive, from time to time, a brief official notification from the Water Authority that, in order to carry out repairs or alterations to the main, water supply will be cut off for a few hours.

For a household without a storage cistern such a notice means the immediate filling of every available bucket and water container for lavatory flushing, food preparation and cooking. The householder with a storage cistern of reasonable capacity can view a notification of this kind with equanimity. He knows that, provided that water supply is resumed within a few hours, only the cold tap over the kitchen sink will fail.

Where should the cold water storage cistern be situated? The traditional site is in the roof space though in recent years it has been suggested that, as a frost precaution, it is better situated at a lower level, perhaps in an upper part of a hall or bathroom airing cupboard. On balance the storage cistern is probably better retained in its traditional position and other measures taken to protect it from frost.

In an airing cupboard a storage cistern can create annoyance from noise (no ball valve is *entirely* silent in operation) and trouble can result from condensation of moisture from the warm damp air of the airing cupboard on its cold surface. Then too, a reduction in height inevitably means a reduction in water pressure. Flushing cisterns will refill more slowly, pressure at hot and cold bathroom taps will be reduced and the provision of a conventional shower on the same floor as the storage cistern will become impossible.

Within the roof space the cistern should be sited well away from the eaves, preferably near a partition wall that will help to support the weight of the cistern and the water it contains and, if possible, immediately above the hot water storage cylinder. However well the latter may be lagged *some* warmth will seep upwards to help to protect the cistern from frost. If it is intended to install a shower on the floor below it is wise to raise the level of the storage cistern. This can be done by constructing a substantial wooden platform for it, so as to raise it three feet or so above the roof timbers.

In the past it was usual to install cisterns of relatively low capacity—25 gal where a hot water system only was to be supplied and 40 gal where the cistern was also intended to serve bathroom cold taps and the w.c. flushing cistern.

Domestic demands for water have increased in recent years as a result of the popularity of washing machines, dish washers and (perhaps) more frequent bathing. Nowadays domestic cold water storage cisterns are standardised at a capacity of 227 litres (50 gal) though smaller sizes are available. It should be noted that this refers to *actual* capacity; that is, to capacity when filled to normal water level, about 4½in from the cistern's rim. The accompanying table gives a guide to the capacity of existing galvanised steel cold water storage cisterns. The figures, which are given in imperial measurements only, since

Nominal capacity (to rim) (gal)	Actual capacity (gal)	Length (in)	Width (in)	Depth (in)
25	15	24	17	17
40	25	27	20	20
60	42	30	23	24
70	50	36	24	23

an existing cistern will certainly have been installed before metrication, illustrate the very considerable difference between 'nominal' and 'actual' capacity.

When faced with the need to replace an existing storage cistern with one of a more appropriate capacity, the dimensions of the trap door giving access to the roof space may appear to present an insoluble problem. A full sized cistern will not pass through many existing trap doors and to enlarge the access makes a substantial increase to the size (and cost) of the replacement job.

Round polythene cisterns can often be flexed through relatively small openings but, if all else fails, storage capacity can be increased by linking two smaller cisterns together by means of a 28mm (1in) pipe 2in above the bases of the cisterns. Where this is done it is important to ensure that the distribution pipes are taken from one cistern and that the ball-valve inlet is connected to the other. This will ensure a steady flow of water through both cisterns and avoid any risk of stagnation.

The traditional cold water storage cistern is constructed of galvanised steel. Cisterns of this material are tough, generally long lasting and offer good support to the water supply pipe. They are however heavy, not too easy to clean thoroughly and—above all— are subject to corrosion.

Members of the older generation of plumbers frequently express surprise and disgust at the fact that in a modern home, a galvanised steel cistern may show serious evidence of corrosion within four or five years of installation whereas they have known similar cisterns, installed in pre-war houses, to remain untouched by rust for half a century. This is not entirely due, as they probably imagine, to the inferiority of modern manufacturing methods. It is explained by the almost universal post-war substitution of copper for lead or iron supply and distributing pipes.

If connected rods of zinc and copper are immersed in a weak acid (an electrolyte) a simple electric cell is produced. Electric current passes from one rod to the other. Bubbles of hydrogen gas form in the electrolyte and the zinc dissolves away. Similar conditions are produced when copper tubing is connected to a galvanised steel storage cistern. The water in the cistern will, if slightly acid, act as the electrolyte. The zinc coating of the galvanised steel will dissolve away and permit water to attack the steel underneath. This process is called electrolytic corrosion.

One way of preventing this process is to ensure, by protective internal painting, that water does not come into direct contact with the galvanised steel. When installing a new cistern cut the holes for the pipe connections and apply the treatment before making the actual connections. Roughen the entire internal surface of the cistern with abrasive paper to form a key and then apply two coats of a *tasteless and odourless* bitumastic paint. Several manufacturers produce a paint suitable for this purpose. Make sure that the entire internal surface is coated, paying particular attention to the areas in the immediate vicinity of the holes cut for the pipe connections. Install the cistern when the paint has dried thoroughly.

This method of protection can also be used to prolong indefinitely the life of a cistern that is already showing serious signs of corrosion. Drain and dry the cistern thoroughly and preferably disconnect the supply and distributing pipes. Remove every trace of existing rust with abrasive paper or by wire brushing—use goggles to protect the eyes when using a wire brush. This process may well leave deep pit marks in the metal, possibly even holes penetrating right through it. Such holes and pitmarks may be filled with one of the many epoxy resin fillers now on the market used in accordance with the manufacturer's instructions.

When the filler has set apply two coats of bitumastic paint as suggested for a new cistern. It is not generally necessary to roughen the internal surface of an old cistern to form a key. This treatment will prolong the useful life of the cistern for several years and can be repeated when it becomes necessary.

Galvanised steel cisterns which are not already showing signs of corrosion can also be protected by means of a sacrificial anode. This method makes use of the same principle that is responsible for electrolytic corrosion. All metals have a fixed electric potential and, when electrolytic action takes place, it is the metal with the higher potential that dissolves away. Anodic protection takes advantage of the fact that magnesium has a considerably higher potential than either zinc or copper.

A sacrificial anode is a lump of magnesium suspended in the water of the cistern and maintained (usually by means of a piece of copper wire clamped to the cistern rim) in electrical contact with the metal of the cistern (*Figure 2.1*). The magnesium dissolves away (is sacrificed) and the zinc coating of the galvanised steel is protected. Anodic protection has been

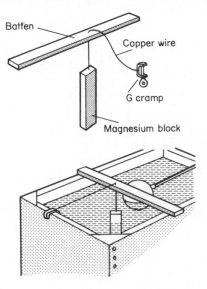

Fig. 2.1. Preventing corrosion by means of a sacrificial anode

found to be most effective in hard water areas. Unlike internal painting it can be adapted to protect galvanised steel hot water storage tanks as well as cold water storage cisterns. Although, as we have seen, galvanised steel cisterns can be protected from corrosion, cisterns made of non-corrodible materials have obvious advantages.

Non-metallic cisterns

Asbestos cement cisterns come into this category but they are not without their drawbacks. They are heavy—a cistern with a capacity of 50 gal weighs 104 lb. They are liable to accidental damage and to damage from frost. They must be handled with care. Holes should not be cut nearer than 4in to the base of the cistern and, since the material of which they are made is ½in thick, hole cutting can present difficulties.

Cisterns made of modern plastic materials have the advantages of asbestos cement cisterns without their disadvantages. They are, of course, quite non-corrodible and have smooth and easily cleaned internal surfaces. They are light in weight so that one-man installation is a practical possibility. Since the plastic of which they are made is a poor conductor of heat they offer a measure of built-in frost protection.

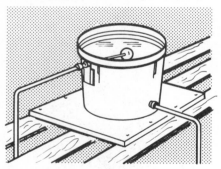

Fig. 2.2. Marley round polythene cistern

Round, flexible polythene cisterns (*Figure 2.2*) have already been mentioned. There are as well a number of rectangular plastic cisterns (*Figure 2.3*) on the market, some reinforced with fibreglass for extra strength. The author's home has a plastic/fibreglass storage cistern that was installed ten years ago and is, quite literally, 'as new'.

Plastic cisterns are easily installed but there are a number of important points that must be borne in mind. Plastic cisterns must rest on a flat, level base—never just on the roof timbers. A piece of chipboard or two or three pieces of floor board spiked to the roof timbers are quite satisfactory. Cut the holes for the tappings with a saw hole cutter fitted into a

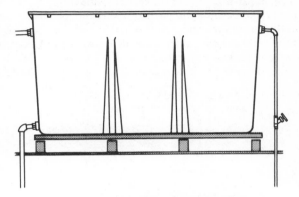

Fig. 2.3. An Osmaflow plastic cistern

drill or brace. Cut from inside with a block of wood placed under the cistern wall for support.

Make sure that all pipe connections are taken squarely to the cistern walls so as to avoid stressing the plastic. For each connection use two large washers—one metal and one plastic— on each side of the cistern wall. The plastic washer should be in direct contact with the cistern wall, followed by the metal washer and back nut. *Never* use boss white or other water-proofing material in direct contact with the walls of a plastic cistern. It is quite unnecessary and could damage the plastic.

Remember that a plastic cistern does not offer the same support to the rising main as does a galvanised steel or asbestos cement cistern. When fitting a ball-valve to a round polythene cistern always use the metal supporting plate supplied with the cistern. Secure the rising main firmly to the roof timbers. Failure to observe these final points can lead to intolerable noise and vibration as the cistern fills with water.

Whatever the material the cistern is made from, it should be fitted with a dust and vermin-proof but not airtight cover. This is both a frost precaution and a safeguard against contamination. The water from the cistern will not be used for drinking but it will be used for teeth cleaning!

The walls, but not the base, of the cistern should be lagged with fibreglass tank lagging material or—in the case of rectangular cisterns—with purpose made expanded polystyrene or strawboard lagging units (*Figure 2.4*). This precaution is less essential with plastic cisterns than with those of other materials.

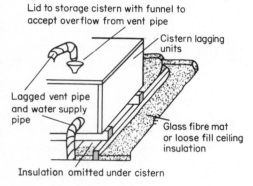

Fig. 2.4. Roof space frost protection

The base of the cistern should not be lagged and if, to conserve warmth in the rooms below, a fibreglass blanket or loose fill lagging material, has been laid between the joists, this should be omitted from the area immediately beneath the cistern. There is, in fact, something to be said for extending the lagging material downwards from the base of the cistern to the ceiling below, to provide a channel via which slightly warmer air can be funnelled up towards the base of the cistern.

One other vital frost precaution relates to the one connection to the cold water storage cistern that has not so far been mentioned—the overflow or warning pipe. This pipe, which should be at least 22mm (¾in) in diameter, connects to the cistern below the level of the ball-valve inlet and about 1in above normal water level. Its purpose is *not* to give indefinite protection against overflow in the event of a ball-valve failure but to give warning that this has occurred. It should therefore discharge in plain view in the open air. A steady drip—much less a full-bore flow—from this pipe should never be ignored.

The warning pipe obviously provides a route by which icy draughts can penetrate to the vulnerable plumbing fittings of the roof space unless proper precautions are taken. The traditional method of protection is to provide a hinged copper flap at the external end of the overflow pipe (*Figure 2.5*).

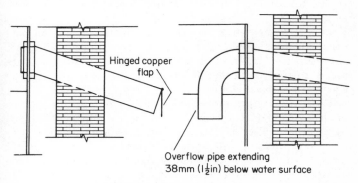

Fig. 2.5. Frost protection for the overflow warning pipe; left, external protection; right, internal protection

Wind blowing against the end of the pipe will close the flap and will be prevented from entering the pipe. Unfortunately, through disuse, these flaps often jam open and fail to function when required.

A better and more modern method of protection is to continue the warning pipe *inside* the cistern and to bend it over so that its open end is a couple of inches or so below the water surface. A trap is thus formed which prevents cold air from blowing up the pipe. Plastic screw-on extension pieces are available to enable this form of protection to be given to existing warning pipes.

Ball-valves (or float-valves)

Strictly speaking the word 'cistern' should be used to describe water storage vessels open to atmospheric pressure—the main cold water storage cistern, w.c. flushing cisterns and the small feed and expansion cistern that supplies the primary circuit of an indirect hot water system (see Chapter 3). 'Tanks' are enclosed vessels and the use of this word, in domestic plumbing, is restricted by the purists to galvanised steel hot water tanks sometimes used for hot water supply.

As however these tanks are increasingly being replaced by copper hot water storage cylinders and can therefore be regarded as obsolescent, there is a growing tendency to refer to the main cold water storage *tank* and, particularly, to the feed and expansion *tank*. However much this may irritate traditional plumbers—and writers of plumbing text books!—this change of use is part of the evolution of the English language and to ignore it is to cause confusion.

Cisterns and open tanks are supplied with water by means of ball-valves or float-valves. Like many other plumbing fittings these valves have experienced revolutionary changes of design over the past half century. Depending upon the age of the installation the householder, or plumber, may find any one of five ball-valves of quite distinct design in current use—and there are a number of sub-species.

All ball-valves operate by means of a float (not necessarily a 'ball') fixed to the end of a rigid float arm of brass or plastic. As water is drawn off from the cistern the water level falls and the float falls with it. This movement is transmitted via the float arm to the valve itself which opens to allow water to flow into the cistern. When the water in the cistern—and the float— reach a predetermined level, the float arm closes the valve and flow of water ceases.

The oldest, simplest—and least satisfactory—kind of ball-valve likely to be encountered today is that of the *Croydon pattern*. As can be seen from *Figure 2.6* this valve has a vertical outlet, closed by a washered plug connected to the float arm. As water level in the cistern falls the plug is pulled away from the valve seating and, noisily and with a great deal of splashing, water flows into the cistern via two channels constructed on either side of the valve body. The inherent, and incurable, noisiness of this kind of valve is its main disadvantage. It is

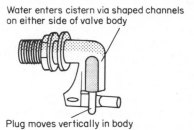

Fig. 2.6. The Croydon ball valve

quite suitable, and is often used, for cattle watering troughs and for static water storage cisterns on municipal allotments. Few people nowadays would wish to have one in the home.

The ball valve in commonest domestic use—certainly in installations dating from before the 1960s—is that of the *Portsmouth pattern.* These valves are quieter than Croydon

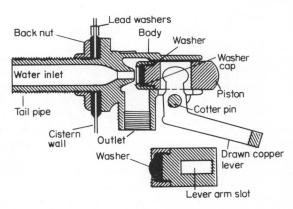

Fig. 2.7. The Portsmouth pattern ball valve

valves if for no other reason than that water flows from the valve outlet in a single stream. As can be seen in *Figure 2.7* the washered plug of the Portsmouth valve moves horizontally in the valve body. A slot in this plug accommodates the angled end of the float arm and the plug therefore moves to and fro as water level rises or falls.

It used to be the practice to enhance the silent action of this valve by screwing a 'silencer tube' of metal or plastic into the valve outlet so that incoming water was discharged into the cistern below the level of water already there. Water Authorities now forbid the use of these silencer tubes because of the risk of back siphonage in the event of a failure of mains pressure, which could result in mains water being contaminated by water from a storage cistern. This prohibition will undoubtedly hasten the changeover from the Portsmouth valve to those of more inherently silent action.

Common faults to which both Croydon and Portsmouth valves are prone are as follows.

Plug sticking in valve body resulting in failure to open or close properly – This is common in hard water areas and is due to the formation of hard water scale on the plug and the interior surfaces of the valve body.

To remedy first cut off the water supply to the valve. Pull out the split pin on which the float arm pivots and remove the float arm. The plug of a Croydon valve will now fall out into the hand.

Some Portsmouth valves have a screw-on cap at the end of the valve body. This cap must be unscrewed and removed. Then insert the blade of a screw driver into the slot under the valve body from which the end of the float arm has been removed. Push the plug out of the open end of the valve body.

Clean the plug and the interior of the valve body with fine abrasive paper. Smear the plug lightly with petroleum jelly and reassemble.

Valve fails to close properly because of washer failure – This is indicated by a steady drip of water from the overflow or warning pipe of the cistern. To renew the valve washer dismantle the valve and remove the plug as indicated above.

The plug is in two parts—a body and a retaining cap. The body should be held securely in a vice and the retaining cap unscrewed with a pair of pliers. The old washer can then be replaced with a new one. The retaining cap of a long-installed valve can be extremely difficult to remove. Rather than risk damaging the plug it is better to pick the old washer out from under the rim of the retaining cap and to force the new washer under this rim. If you take this course of action you should make sure that the washer lies flat in its seating before reassembling.

Continued dripping from the overflow pipe after the ball valve washer has been renewed suggests that the valve seating is scored by grit from the main. Although it is possible, with a special tool, to reseat the ball valve it is usually as cheap (and easier) to renew the valve.

Slow filling or leaking past the valve despite the fact that washer and seating are sound—Either of these faults suggests that a valve of the wrong pressure classification has been installed. Ball valves are classified as 'high pressure', 'medium pressure', 'low pressure' or 'fullway' according to the diameter of the nozzle orifice. They are usually stamped HP, LP etc. on the valve body to indicate the pressure for which they are intended.

Except where mains pressure is unusually low, ball valves serving cisterns supplied direct from the main should be high pressure. Those serving flushing cisterns supplied from a main storage cistern should be low pressure. Where a flushing cistern is supplied from a low level storage cistern—perhaps in the upper part of an airing cupboard only a few feet above the level of the w.c. suite—a fullway valve will ensure rapid recovery.

Noisy filling—Noise may arise both from the sound of inflowing water and from water hammer and vibration in the plumbing system. Water hammer and vibration arise from ripple formation on the surface of the water as water flows into an almost full cistern.

These ripples may make the valve bounce on its seating to produce water hammer. They may also shake the float arm up and down and to and fro. This movement is transmitted to the cold water supply pipe which, particularly if it is of copper, will act as a sounding board to amplify the vibration out of all recognition. It used to be the practice to use the silencer tube already mentioned to reduce ripple formation and the consequent noise. This has now been prohibited but there are still measures that can be taken to improve the situation.

Purpose made stabilisers are available in the form of a plastic disc and a short plastic arm that clips onto the float arm so that the disc is suspended in the cistern a few inches below the level of the float. This will do something to ensure that the float does not bounce on every ripple. Make sure that the rising main is securely fixed to the roof timbers and is not supported solely by the wall of the cistern. This is particularly important where the cistern is of plastic material.

Yet another course of action is to cut out the final metre (3ft) or so of the rising main and replace it with polythene tubing. This will not amplify the sound as copper tubing does. Or, of course, one can fit a ball-valve of a different pattern.

Equilibrium ball valves are particularly useful in areas where mains water pressure is subject to fluctuation because they operate quite independently of the pressure of water behind them. They are also very helpful in eliminating water hammer. A great deal of the 'bounce' that causes water hammer is due to the conflicting forces of water pressure within the main and the buoyancy of the ball valve float.

Equilibrium valves can be made in either the Croydon or the Portsmouth pattern and a Portsmouth pattern equilibrium valve is shown in *Figure 2.8*. The essential feature is that the plug of the valve has a channel passing through it to a watertight chamber at the rear of the valve. The plug therefore has to have a second washer at the rear to ensure the watertightness of this chamber. The effect of this design is that water pressure is equal on each side of the plug. Mains pressure is not continually trying to force the valve open and the plug moves *solely* in response to the rise and fall of the float. This enables the valve to have a wide nozzle orifice which ensures rapid replenishment of the cistern even when pressure is low.

Some ten years ago, at the Government's Building Research Station at Garston, a new and revolutionary ball valve was

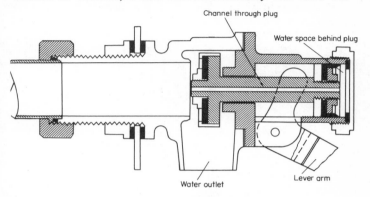

Fig. 2.8. Portsmouth pattern equilibrium valve

developed with the intention of reducing the noise and other drawbacks to which traditional valves are subject. These are sold under various trade names and are referred to generally as *Garston, B.R.S.* or *diaphragm ball valves.*

The moving plug was completely eliminated and the silent and score-resistant nylon nozzle is closed by means of a large diameter rubber diaphragm. The end of the float arm presses a small metal or plastic plunger against this diaphragm to close the valve. There are few moving parts and these are protected from the scaling effect of contact with water by the rubber diaphragm. Another useful feature of this kind of valve is that it can be dismantled by hand, by turning the large knurled retaining nut.

B.R.S. valves are manufactured in brass or plastic. They all incorporate some means of adjusting the water level in the cistern without recourse to bending the float arm. Early models were fitted with a silencer tube (*Figure 2.9*). Since these have been prohibited manufacturers have produced models with an overhead outlet and a device by means of which water enters the cistern in a relatively silent spray (*Figure 2.10*). Another feature of recently manufactured B.R.S. valves is the demountable nozzle. This permits any valve to be dismantled and rapidly converted from high pressure to low pressure operation or vice versa as required.

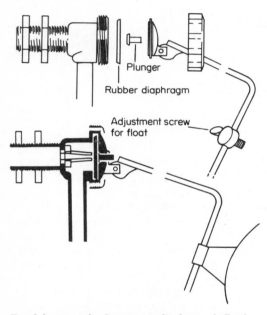

Fig. 2.9. An early Garston or diaphragm ball valve with silencer tube

The very latest design of ball valve is the diaphragm/ equilibrium or diaphragm/servo valve, of which the first model on the market was the Torbeck made by Ideal Standard Ltd. This incorporates some of the features of the conventional equilibrium ball valve and some of the diaphragm or B.R.S. valve.

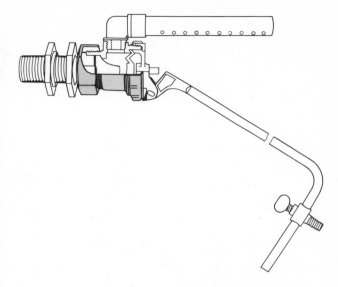

Fig. 2.10. Peglers diaphragm ball valve with overhead outlet

The Torbeck, like a conventional equilibrium ball valve, has a water chamber—the 'servo chamber'—behind the diaphragm closing the nozzle aperture (*Figure 2.11*). Water flows into this chamber via the metering pin opening but is prevented from passing through into the cistern, when this is full of water, by a sealing washer on the float arm which closes the pilot hole. When water level in the cistern falls, the descent of the float arm opens the pilot hole and water can flow out, reducing the pressure in the servo chamber. Pressure of water on the inlet side of the valve then opens the diaphragm and water can pass through the outlet.

The Torbeck has an overhead outlet. This is fitted with a collapsible plastic silencer tube, which reduces the noise of water delivery but—because it is collapsible—is immune to the risk of back siphonage. The design of the valve has permitted the use of a very small float and short float arm. It has a wide

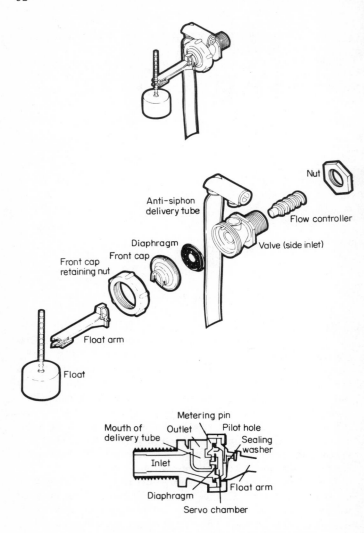

Nut

Anti-siphon
delivery tube

Flow controller

Diaphragm

Front cap

Valve (side inlet)

Front cap
retaining nut

Float arm

Float

Metering pin

Mouth of
delivery tube

Outlet

Pilot hole

Sealing
washer

Inlet

Diaphragm

Float arm

Servo chamber

Fig. 2.11. The Torbeck equilibrium diaphragm valve

nozzle aperture, permitting rapid filling. A flow controller is provided for use where the valve is connected direct to a mains supply.

Failure of all types of diaphragm valve is most likely to occur as a result of debris from the main entering the space between the nozzle and the diaphragm and blocking it, either partially or completely. Diaphragm/equilibrium valves can also fail as a result of quite small grit particles from the main obstructing the metering pin hole or the pilot hole.

At the time of writing this type of valve could be regarded as being still in the experimental stage and it is probable that later models will overcome this vulnerability to obstruction.

3 Domestic Hot Water Supply

Plumbers and heating engineers are sometimes asked by anxious householders, 'What is the *best* means of hot water supply?'.

The only honest answer to this question is that there is no *best* means universally applicable to all situations. In deciding upon the best means of hot water supply for his client the installer should consider the design of the house and, perhaps, the way of life of its residents. The best system for a family where there are a number of children and the housewife is at home all day may well be quite uneconomical for an identical house where husband and wife are both at work and are likely to require hot water only for relatively brief periods in the morning and evening.

In some homes—not necessarily particularly large ones— the best solution to the problem of whole-house hot water supply may be to use one means for part of the house and another means for heating water for, for instance, a shower or a wash-basin in an external or otherwise remote w.c. compartment.

There is no doubt that some form of cylinder storage system provides the most popular and most versatile means of domestic hot water supply. Systems of this kind can be operated by electricity, solid fuel, gas or oil or by a combination of these. A cylinder storage hot water system can also be used in conjunction with a central heating system, using the same heat source.

Cylinder storage systems depend for their efficiency upon the fact that water expands in volume when heated while its weight remains unchanged. Thus a gallon (or a litre) of hot water weighs less than the same volume of cold water. Hot water therefore 'floats' on top of cold, or cooler, water. This principle is used to ensure continuous circulation between the boiler and hot water storage vessel. It also ensures that the hottest stored water remains in the upper part of the vessel, immediately available for use.

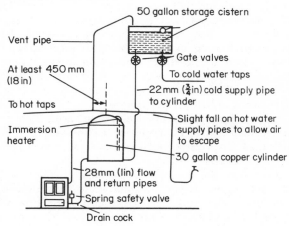

Fig. 3.1. A simple direct cylinder hot water supply system

A simple 'direct cylinder' hot water system is illustrated in *Figure 3.1*. Cold water flows from the cold water storage cistern to the cylinder through a 22mm (¾in) or 28mm (1in) supply pipe connected to the cylinder horizontally at a point near to its base.

Hot water distribution pipes to the various hot taps are taken from another 22mm (¾in) or 28mm (1in) pipe connected to a tapping at the apex of the cylinder dome. This pipe is continued upwards to terminate open ended over the cold water storage cistern and thus to serve as a vent pipe for the hot water system. It should be noted that the system then forms an open ended 'U' tube and that the level of water in the vent pipe will be the same as that in the storage cistern.

If the cylinder is to be heated solely by means of an electric immersion heater there will be no other plumbing connections to it. The boiler flow and return tappings in the side of the cylinder will be blanked off and a drain cock must be provided at the base of the cold water supply pipe to the cylinder to permit it to be drained if required.

If, on the other hand, a boiler is to be used to heat the water this should ideally be situated as close to the cylinder as possible but at a lower level. A 28mm (1in) flow pipe is taken from the upper connection of the boiler to the upper, or flow, connection of the cylinder. A similar return pipe is taken from the lower, or return, cylinder connection to the lower connection of the boiler. In a well-designed system the flow and return pipes will be quite short and will rise steeply all the way from the boiler to the cylinder tappings.

A drain cock should be provided at the lowest point of the return pipe adjacent to the boiler. It is also wise to provide a spring loaded safety valve on either the flow or return pipe as close to the boiler as possible.

It is usual to position this safety valve on the flow pipe but the return pipe is equally appropriate and this position does, in fact, offer a slight advantage. Scale formation, which *could* produce a build-up of pressure, is more likely to occur at the flow tapping than at the return tapping. Such a build-up of pressure would not affect a safety valve fitted to the flow pipe but it would be released from a valve fitted into the return pipe.

When the boiler is first lit water in it is heated. It expands and becomes lighter. Colder and heavier water from the return pipe flows into the boiler beneath it and pushes the heated water up the flow pipe into the upper part of the cylinder. This phenomenon is often described by saying that 'hot water rises' which is not quite true. To understand the principle of circulation it must be appreciated that hot water does not rise of its own volition. It is pushed upwards by colder and heavier water flowing into the boiler beneath it.

Circulation will continue for as long as the boiler fire is alight. Hot water stored in the cylinder will spread downwards until this vessel is full of hot water. As this is drawn off from the hot taps cold water will flow into the lower part of the cylinder from the cold water storage cistern. This will, in its turn, pass down the return pipe into the boiler to be heated.

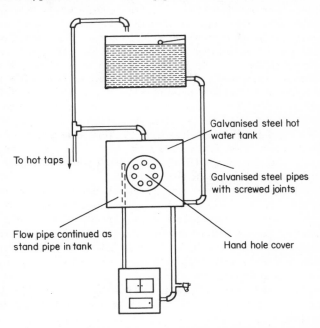

To hot taps

Galvanised steel hot water tank

Galvanised steel pipes with screwed joints

Flow pipe continued as stand pipe in tank

Hand hole cover

Fig. 3.2. Typical arrangement of a direct cylinder hot water system using galvanised steel pipes and tank

Many dwellings built before 1940 will be found to have a hot water system similar to that already described but with galvanised steel, instead of copper, circulating and distributing pipes and with a rectangular galvanised steel hot water storage *tank* instead of a copper cylinder (*Figure 3.2*). A rectangular tank of this kind may be easier to accommodate in an airing cupboard. It may also be easier to lag effectively to prevent heat loss. There are however serious disadvantages.

The rectangular shape means that it is more liable to distortion or damage from internal pressure. Where a hot water storage tank is installed the cold water storage cistern must usually be situated no higher than the floor immediately above. It is not possible—as it is with a cylinder—to have the hot water storage vessel on the ground floor of a two-storey house and the cold water cistern in the roof space. Then too, since hot water is more corrosive than cold, galvanised steel hot water tanks are even more subject to corrosion than galvanised steel cisterns. Nor can they, like cold water cisterns, be protected by internal painting.

Because of the risk of electrolytic action (see previous chapter) extensions to a galvanised steel hot water system should never be made with copper tubing. Where extensions are required it is best to use modern stainless steel tubing. This is scarcely more difficult to use than copper and does not present any risk of electrolytic action.

When fitting a replacement galvanised steel hot water tank an essential precaution against corrosion is to ensure that every trace of metal dust or shaving—resulting from cutting the holes for the pipe connections—is carefully removed. Any such metal fragments, however small, left in the base of the tank will unfailingly become a focus for corrosion and will lead to rapid tank failure.

Galvanised steel hot water tanks are provided with a circular hand-hole, sealed by a rubber gasket and a bolted-down hand-hole cover, to give access to the interior of the tank. Should it be necessary to remove this cover, never overlook the fact that, with all hot water. storage systems of this kind, the hot water distribution pipes are taken from the top of the storage vessel. When water has been cut off to the cold water storage cistern and the hot taps opened and drained, *the hot water storage tank or cylinder is still full of water.* It cannot be drained from the hot taps. Before attempting to unbolt the hand-hole cover drain from the drain-cock beside the boiler—or at the base of the cold water supply pipe.

Installers are often faced with the problem of providing a piped hot water supply to a pre-war house that was previously without this amenity or, where such a house has been divided into two or more self-contained flats, providing a separate hot water system for each flat.

To meet this need cheap and space-saving 'packaged' hot water systems have been produced. These consist of a hot water storage cylinder and cold water storage cistern combined in one unit—sometimes called a two-in-one tank. These preserve the essential features of a cylinder storage hot water system but, of course, with much shortened cold water supply and vent pipes.

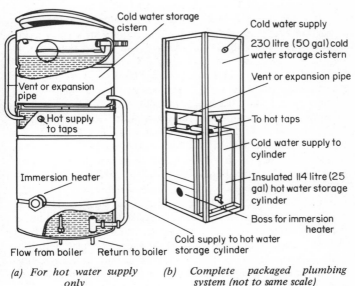

(a) *For hot water supply only*   (b) *Complete packaged plumbing system (not to same scale)*

Fig. 3.3. Packaged 'two-in-one' systems

One such unit has a 25 gal or 30 gal capacity hot water cylinder with a relatively small (15 gal or 20 gal) round copper cistern immediately above it (*Figure 3.3a*). A small cistern of this kind is capable of supplying only the hot water storage cylinder and is therefore of little value in areas where the Water Authority forbids the connection of w.c. flushing cisterns and bathroom cold taps direct to the main. Other units have a full-sized 50 gal capacity storage cistern (*Figure 3.3b*). These may be regarded as complete 'packaged plumbing systems'. They need only provision of a heat source and connection to supply and distributing pipes.

Such packaged plumbing systems must, of course, be situated so that the base of the cold tank is above the level of any draw-off point. It will, for instance, be impossible to install a conventional shower on the same floor as such a unit though, of course, one could be installed on the floor below.

Although direct cylinder storage hot water systems provide a reliable and trouble-free hot water supply in a great many homes, they are subject to damage and deterioration from two causes—rust and scale. Rusting may take place within the boiler. This will be indicated when discoloured, rusty water flows from the hot taps—particularly when a considerable volume of hot water has been drawn off.

Boiler scale can present an even more serious problem. Hard water will be discussed in some detail in a later chapter. Here it is sufficient to say that when hard water (which means most water supplies in southern and central Britain) is heated to a temperature of about 70°C (160°F) calcium carbonate—boiler scale or fur—is deposited. This can be seen on the interior surfaces of any kettle in regular use in such an area.

The first indication of scale formation in a domestic boiler is loss of efficiency. Scale insulates the water in the boiler from the heat source and the water takes longer to heat. Later, as scale deposits increase, hissing, bubbling and banging sounds will be heard as overheated water is forced through ever-diminishing channels. Scale does not *only* insulate the water in the boiler from the heat source. It also insulates the metal of the boiler from the cooling effect of the circulating water. Deprived of this protection the metal of the boiler will slowly burn away and, eventually, one of the most disastrous of plumbing emergencies—a leaking boiler—will result.

Another problem arises when a direct cylinder storage hot water system is used to heat a radiator or towel rail. Modern pressed steel radiators should *never* be connected to such a system as they will very rapidly corrode. It was considered permissible to connect a cast iron or copper radiator to a direct system and it is not unusual to use a system of this kind to heat a towel rail of non-corrodible material. This never works very satisfactorily in practice as the purpose of the storage cylinder is to conserve the heat in the stored water and the purpose of the radiator or towel rail is to dissipate it. When a large volume of hot water is drawn off for a bath—the time that the towel rail is most required—the towel rail will run cold.

Indirect cylinder storage hot water system

These difficulties can be overcome by the provision of an *indirect* cylinder storage hot water system (*Figure 3.4*). With a system of this kind the water heated in the boiler passes through the cylinder in a closed coil or heat exchanger thus heating the domestic hot water *indirectly*.

The flow and return pipes, together with the heat exchanger, are referred to as the primary circuit. It is supplied with water from a small 'feed and expansion' or header tank and it is a vital design feature that the domestic hot water and the water in the primary circuit are kept entirely separate. As its name indicates the purpose of the feed and expansion tank is to accommodate the expansion of the primary circuit when it is heated as well as to ensure that this circuit is supplied with water. For this reason the ball-valve feeding this tank should be adjusted to give only two or three inches of water in the tank when the system is first filled. When heated the water in the primary circuit will expand into the tank and rise above the level of the ball valve float.

Water from the primary circuit is never drawn off in normal use and only the very small losses arising from evaporation are made up from the feed and expansion tank. This accounts for

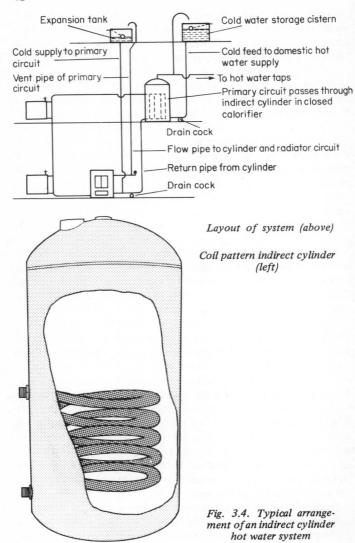

Expansion tank

Cold water storage cistern

Cold supply to primary circuit

Cold feed to domestic hot water supply

Vent pipe of primary circuit

To hot water taps

Primary circuit passes through indirect cylinder in closed calorifier

Drain cock

Flow pipe to cylinder and radiator circuit

Return pipe from cylinder

Drain cock

Layout of system (above)

Coil pattern indirect cylinder (left)

Fig. 3.4. Typical arrangement of an indirect cylinder hot water system

the relative freedom from corrosion and scale of indirect hot water systems. Dissolved air gives water its corrosive quality. This is driven off from the water in the primary circuit when it is first heated. Similarly, any given volume of water contains only a given quantity of scale-forming chemicals. These are precipitated on the internal surface of the boiler when it is first heated and, thereafter, no more scale will form. Any towel rail, radiator or central heating circuit should be connected to the primary circuit. The effect of drawing off a large volume of hot water will have far less effect upon it.

Central heating does not come within the scope of this book. However it must be mentioned that, where a central heating system is installed in conjunction with an indirect hot water system, freedom from corrosion is only *relative.* Some air will always be present in the primary circuit as a result of minute leaks too small to permit water to escape and as a result of air dissolving into the surface of the water in the feed and expansion tank.

Where pressed steel radiators are used with copper circulating pipes a form of electrolytic corrosion can take place. The metal of the radiators slowly corrodes away and hydrogen and black iron oxide sludge, or magnetite, are produced. These obstruct circulation and the corrosive qualities of the magnetite are a common cause of early circulating pump failure. This corrosion can be prevented by the introduction of a reliable chemical corrosion inhibitor into the feed and expansion tank.

The conventional indirect hot water system requires a separate feed and expansion tank. There are however on the market patent self-priming indirect cylinders, of which the primatic is the best known, which require no separate feed tank.

A purpose made heat exchanger or 'inner cylinder' permits water to spill over from the domestic hot water system into the primary circuit when the system is first filled (*Figure 3.5*). It is prevented from returning to mix with the domestic hot water by an air lock that is automatically produced.

Some scepticism has been expressed about the effectiveness of self-priming cylinders of this kind. Experience suggests that they provide effective separation of the primary and domestic water so long as the boiler is never permitted actually to boil (this should, in any case, always be avoided) and the particular

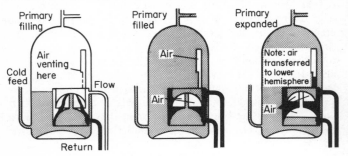

Fig. 3.5. How a primatic self-priming indirect cylinder works

model of self-priming cylinder is large enough to accommodate the expansion of the primary, and any radiator, circuit when heated.

Electric water heating

An electric immersion heater is frequently fitted into a hot water storage cylinder served by a boiler to provide a supply of hot water during the summer months. On the other hand one or more immersion heaters may be fitted into a storage cylinder to provide the sole means of hot water supply. Most manufacturers of electric appliances manufacture cylinders, complete with immersion heaters, designed to meet this need (*Figure 3.6a*). Usually installed under the draining board of the kitchen sink they are, for this reason, often called 'under draining board' or UDB heaters.

Typically, UDB heaters have very heavy built-in insulation and are provided with two horizontally aligned electric immersion heaters. The upper element is kept permanently switched on to meet the small, but frequent, demands of hot water for washing up, washing and shaving and so on. The

lower element is intended to be switched on an hour or so
before greater volumes of hot water are required for baths or
laundry purposes. Most UDB heaters need a separate cold

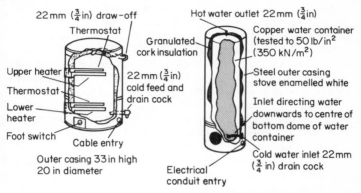

The 'under draining board' (UDB)   Off-peak electric water heater
            water heater

Fig. 3.6. Two methods of providing hot water by electric heating

water storage cistern in the same way as an ordinary cylinder
storage system does. There are however 'cistern heaters' which
incorporate their own small, cold water supply cistern in the
upper part of the unit.

A variant of the UDB water heater is the off-peak electric
water heater designed to take advantage of the cheaper off-peak
electricity (Figure 3.6b). These are usually tall and slim to
encourage the stratification of the heated water. A spreading
device at the cold water inlet ensures that incoming cold
water spreads evenly over the base of the cylinder and does
not mix with water already heated. Off-peak heaters usually
have a large capacity—50 gal instead of the 25 gal usual with a
UDB heater. Fifty gallons is said to meet the daily demand for
hot water of an average family. The heater is switched on overnight, to take advantage of the off-peak rates. During the day
the electric element is switched off and the stored hot water
is used by the family.

Heat loss

Electricity is a very efficient, but very expensive, heat source. When it is used either as the sole or as a supplementary means of heating stored water there are important design considerations that must be observed if the system is to operate economically. A basic requirement is that the storage cylinder should be *effectively* lagged. Effective lagging is built into the construction of UDB and off-peak heaters but must be provided by the installer or householder for an ordinary copper cylinder.

It has been established that the insulating material used is less important than its thickness and that maximum economy is achieved with a thickness of 3in. An insulated copper cylinder 18in in diameter and 36in high, with a nominal capacity of 30 gal, will lose 86 units of electricity per week if the temperature of the water is maintained at $140°F$ and the air temperature is $60°F$. Raise the water temperature to $160°F$ (the usual storage temperature in soft water areas) and the loss will be 115 units per week. The same cylinder, provided with a 2in thickness of glass fibre lagging, will lose 8.8 units per week. Increase the thickness of the lagging to 3in and the loss will be only 6 units.

The avoidance of long 'dead legs' is another important design consideration. 'Dead legs' are lengths of pipe from the storage cylinder to the draw-off points. After water has been drawn off the water left in the dead leg will rapidly cool and its heat will be wasted. A dead leg of 15mm (½in) copper tubing carrying water at $140°F$ to a sink or basin tap will waste about 0.19 units of electricity per foot run per week. A similar 22mm (¾in) copper tube will waste 0.38 units per foot run per week.

Modern architectural design usually eliminates long dead legs by situating the bathroom and kitchen in close proximity. Where hot water is required at any draw-off point more than about 20ft distant from the storage cylinder it is wise to consider the provision of a small, separate water heater to serve that point only. Above all, electrically heated water must never be permitted to circulate. Circulation of this kind can produce really crippling electricity bills.

Electrically heated water circulating through a 15mm (½in) copper tube at 140°F will waste 1.36 units of electricity *per foot run* per week. The wastage from 28mm (1in) copper tubing will be 2.33 units per foot run per week.

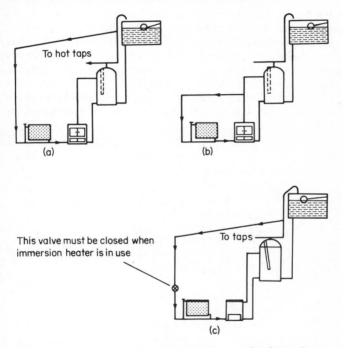

Fig. 3.7. Circulation of hot water through a towel rail or radiator circuit

There are a number of ways in which circulation may take place. The most obvious one is through a towel rail or radiator circuit. Where a towel rail is fitted into a direct hot water system the flow pipe is frequently taken from the vent pipe, above the hot water cylinder. It is dropped onto the towel rail and the return pipe is taken, falling all the way, to the return pipe from the cylinder to the boiler (*Figure 3.7a*).

This arrangement ensures rapid circulation and the elimination of bubbles that could produce an air-lock. It may be permissible where the cylinder is heated only by a boiler but is quite unacceptable where an immersion heater is fitted. In such a case any towel rail circulation should, preferably, be taken from the flow pipe to the cylinder below the level of the electric heating element (*Figure 3.7b*). This will permit the circulation of water heated by the boiler but prevent the circulation of electrically heated water. Where this arrangement is impossible an alternative might be to fit a gate valve into the towel rail circuit and to make sure that this valve is kept tightly shut when the immersion heater is switched on (*Figure 3.7c*).

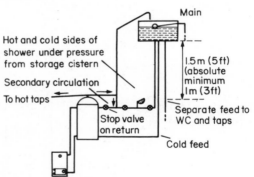

Fig. 3.8. Hot and cold water supplies for a shower installation

Sometimes where there is a long dead-leg serving a shower, for instance, a secondary circulation is arranged as shown in *Figure 3.8* to reduce the delay in the arrival of hot water at the draw-off point. When fitting an immersion heater into a cylinder with a secondary circulation the return should be cut out and eliminated or, alternatively, a gate valve provided to prevent circulation when the immersion heater is switched on.

Reversed circulation may, under certain circumstances, take place between a hot storage cylinder and a cold boiler. This may occur where the cylinder is at only a slightly higher level than the boiler and there is a long horizontal run of flow pipe. It can be prevented by taking the flow pipe to the cylinder at low level and then taking it up to the cylinder flow tapping close to the cylinder wall and within the cylinder lagging jacket (*Figure 3.9a*).

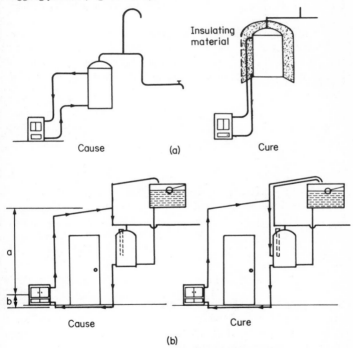

Fig. 3.9. Reverse circulation causes and cures

Sometimes, because of an intervening doorway, the flow pipe from a boiler is taken to connect at high level to the cylinder vent pipe. The return pipe is taken back to the boiler under the floor boards (*Figure 3.9b*). This arrangement will inevitably lead to reversed circulation if an immersion heater is installed.

The best remedy is to reposition either the boiler or the cylinder so that both are on the same side of the doorway. A 'second best' alternative is to provide the flow pipe with an additional vent and to connect it to the cylinder at a point below the level of the immersion heater. This will result in a loss of efficiency and delays in heating the cylinder from the boiler. It will however cut out circulation of electrically heated water.

Finally, there is a risk of 'single pipe circulation' within the vent pipe itself. If this pipe rises vertically from the apex of the cylinder dome currents of hot water may flow up its centre and, cooling, descend against its walls (*Figure 3.10*).

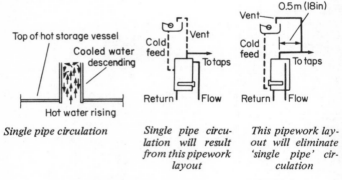

Single pipe circulation

Single pipe circulation will result from this pipework layout

This pipework layout will eliminate 'single pipe' circulation

Fig. 3.10. 'Single pipe' circulation and its prevention

Single pipe circulation can be prevented by bending the vent pipe over as it leaves the cylinder dome and taking it horizontally for a distance of at least 18in before permitting it to rise to the cold water storage cistern.

Instantaneous hot water

Other means of providing domestic hot water supply include 'instantaneous' water heaters and open-outlet water heaters.

The heat source for these appliances may be either electricity or gas. They are generally designed for direct connection to the rising main and thus make it possible (where this is permitted by the Water Authority) to eliminate both the cold water storage cistern and the hot water storage cylinder. Gas still has the advantage for the provision of instantaneous hot water. Small instantaneous heaters are available to supply hot water at a single point and large multipoint models can provide a 'whole house' hot water supply.

The invention and development of the 'balanced flue' has overcome a problem that formerly faced all installers of gas appliances—the safe disposal of the products of combustion. Balanced flue appliances can be installed in any room with an external wall. They involve none of the risks that were associated with the old fashioned gas 'geyser'. Balanced flue appliances are available for both space and water heating. The appliance has its combustion chamber sealed off from the room in which it is fitted. Air intake and flue outlet are situated adjacent to each other on an external wall (*Figure 3.11*). Because they are adjacent they are 'balanced'. Air

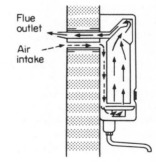

Flue outlet

Air intake

Fig. 3.11. Balanced flue gas water heater

pressure against the flue outlet will be equalled by air pressure against the inlet. The appliance should continue to work satisfactorily no matter how hard the wind may be blowing against the flue outlet.

Electric instantaneous water heaters are a relatively new development but the suspicion with which early models were received has now been largely dispelled. They have the advantage of quick and simple installation in virtually any situation where a water and a power supply are available (*Figure 3.12*).

Fig. 3.12. Electric instantaneous heater supplying basin and shower

They are particularly useful in providing a hot water supply for wash basins in w.c. compartments remote from the main house hot water system and in making possible the provision of a shower in situations where this would otherwise be impossible.

The great advantage of instantaneous water heating is that only water actually *used* is heated. There is no stored water slowly losing its heat and requiring more fuel to restore it. A multipoint gas water heater can therefore be particularly useful to a working husband and wife who require hot water only for relatively short periods in the morning and evening.

A limitation of this kind of appliance that is not always appreciated is the fact that it does not, by its nature, raise a given volume of water *to* a required temperature. It raises the water that passes through it *through* a range of temperatures. During very cold weather, low temperature of water at the inlet will result either in a reduced flow of hot water or a supply of water at a lower temperature. Flow of hot water in gallons per minute is, in any case, generally less than from a storage hot water system.

Open outlet heaters are (usually) small storage heaters designed for direct connection to the rising main (*Figure 3.13*). They may be used over sinks and wash basins where there is no cylinder system or where the use of the storage cylinder would involve an unacceptably long distribution pipe or dead leg.

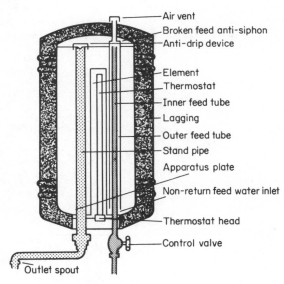

Fig. 3.13. Open outlet electric water heater

The essential feature of the open outlet heater is the position of the control valve. This must be on the inlet side— *not* on the outlet—of the appliance. When hot water is required the inlet control is opened. Cold water flows in to the base of the appliance, displacing stored hot water which overflows through an internal stand-pipe connected to the outlet spout. Modern variations of this kind of appliance may be installed under, instead of over, the sink or wash basin. These must still comply with the essential requirement of a controlled inlet and a free outlet.

Solar heating

Rapidly rising fuel costs in recent years have led heating engineers to give serious consideration to the use of a free source of energy—the sun—to supplement traditional means of water heating. Heat transmitted *by radiation* from the sun is unaffected by air temperature. Even on a cold winter's day the sun's rays can be used to transfer heat to water passing through a purpose-made and specially protected solar panel.

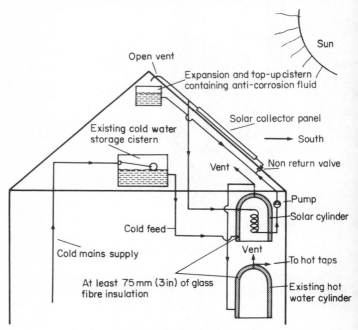

Fig. 3.14. One method of utilising solar heating

Various means of trapping and transmitting this free heat source have been attempted. The one illustrated in *Figure 3.14* is, in my opinion, among the more promising. It is, in effect, an indirect hot water system in which the solar collection panel, heated by the sun, provides a supplementary 'boiler'. A complication is added by the fact that, unlike a conventional boiler, the solar panel must of necessity be situated above the hot water storage cylinder.

This difficulty is overcome by providing two cylinders, one above the other. The upper cylinder is a conventional indirect one in which water from the storage cistern is pre-heated by means of a sealed heat exchanger connected to the solar panel. The lower cylinder may be either direct or indirect and can have, as its main source of heat, either a boiler or an electric immersion heater. Pre-warmed water flows from the top of the upper cylinder to the lower one, from which it is drawn off in the usual way to the hot taps. Water is pumped, in a closed circuit, through the solar panel situated on the southern aspect of the roof's slope. Water passes through the solar panel in small bore copper tubes on a black bed, designed to absorb the radiant heat of the sun.

The solar panel has a glass face, which must be hosed down from time to time for maximum efficiency. This affords protection from the cooling effect of the wind and also has a 'greenhouse' effect, permitting the short wavelength heat rays from the sun to enter but confining the longer wavelength rays reflected from the interior of the solar panel.

Solar heating is still in its infancy but it is not unreasonable to suppose that improved collection, distribution and storage systems will be developed in the years to come. It may well be that financial necessity will dictate that, at least during the summer months, solar energy will, in the future, provide the main heat source for domestic hot water supply.

4 Taps and Mixers

The tap is the basic piece of plumbing equipment. A plumber of the early 1900s, confronted with the taps of today, would find that the differences between these and the old brass taps to which he was accustomed, are more apparent than real.

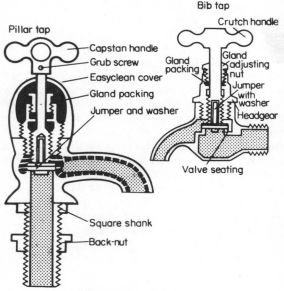

Fig. 4.1. Pillar and bib taps

Although there have been tremendous changes in appearance and design, most modern taps operate in exactly the same way as the bib-cocks that can still be seen protruding over the kitchen sinks of 1914 houses.

Taps are described as 'bibs' or 'pillars'. Bib taps have a horizontal inlet and pillar taps a vertical one (*Figure 4.1*). Pillars are now used for most purposes within the home while bibs are most likely to be found nowadays providing a garden or garage water supply. Water flows into the body of the tap via a threaded 'tail' connected to the distribution pipe. It passes through the valve seating and leaves by the spout. Into the tap body is screwed the 'headgear', a fibre body washer between the two parts of the tap ensuring a watertight joint. The spindle, with a crutch or capstan head, passes through the headgear. Turning the spindle opens or closes the tap by raising or lowering a washered valve or jumper onto the valve seating. When the tap is turned on water is prevented from

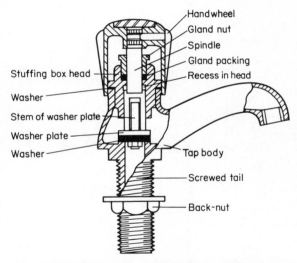

Fig. 4.2. Pillar tap with shrouded head. The section illustrated is the Nuastyle 2 BSS type pillar tap

escaping up the spindle by a gland or stuffing box, packed with greased wool, through which the spindle passes.

Most modern taps have an easy-clean cover that conceals the headgear and many have 'shrouded heads'. With such taps the headgear and the head or handle appear to comprise a single unit (*Figure 4.2*).

Bath and basin mixers are, in effect, two taps with a single spout. Adjusting the two heads produces a single stream of water at the required temperature. Many bath mixers incorporate an upper outlet to supply a flexible shower hose (*Figure 4.3*). A switch is provided to direct the mixed water

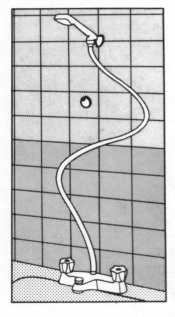

Fig. 4.3. Bath/shower mixer by Barking Brassware Co.

either upwards to the shower or downwards into the bath as required. Some modern basin mixers incorporate a 'pop up' waste. These units dispense with the usual waste plug and somewhat unsightly chain. Pressure on a knob in the centre of the mixer activates a rod and causes the waste plug to 'pop up' and allow the basin to drain (*Figure 4.4*).

Sink mixers are different in design from those used for basins and baths. This is because it is illegal to mix in one fitting water direct from the main (the cold water supply to the kitchen sink) and water from a storage cistern. Consequently sink mixers have separate channels for the hot and cold water passing through the tap body and spout. Hot and cold water mixes *in the air* after leaving the spout.

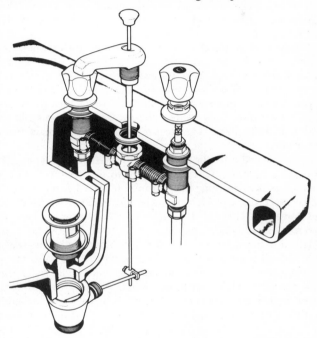

Fig. 4.4. The Bourner basin mixer with pop-up waste plug

Rewashering is the most common maintenance job required on taps. The need for rewashering is indicated when the tap becomes more and more difficult to turn off fully. Eventually, however hard the head is turned, there will still be a steady drip from the spout.

To rewasher any tap of the kind described above the water supply to it must first be cut off. With the cold tap over the sink this is done by turning off the householder's main stop-cock (see Chapter 1). It may be possible to turn off the supply to the hot taps and the bathroom cold taps by turning off any gate valve or stop-cock in the supply pipe. If there is no such control valve the best course of action is to tie up the float arm of the ball valve supplying the main cold water storage cistern and drain this cistern and the distribution pipes. This can be done from the bathroom taps.

Where both hot and cold bathroom taps are supplied from a storage cistern there is no need to drain the hot water from the hot water storage cylinder even if it is a hot tap that is to be rewashered. Turn on the bathroom cold taps and leave to drain. When no more water flows from them turn on the tap to be rewashered. Only the few pints of water in the distributing pipe will drain away. The storage cylinder will remain full of hot water.

Unscrew and raise the easy-clean cover. It should be possible to do this by hand. If it is necessary to use a wrench pad the jaws to avoid damaging the chromium plated surface (*Figure 4.5*). Insert the wrench under the easy-clean cover and turn the hexagonal nut at the base of the headgear. This will unscrew to permit the headgear to be lifted off the tap body. When the headgear is removed the valve, with its washer attached, of a kitchen sink cold tap will be found to be resting on the valve seating. A small retaining nut holds the washer onto the valve. This must be removed or (if this proves difficult) a new washer and jumper complete can be used as a replacement.

Valves of hot taps and bathroom cold taps may be found to be 'pegged' into the headgear of the tap. The valve will turn freely but cannot be removed without breaking the pegging. In such a situation every effort must be made to unscrew the washer retaining nut. A drop of penetrating oil will often loosen it sufficiently to enable it to be unscrewed with a spanner of the correct size. If this proves to be absolutely impossible the valve *can* be removed from the headgear by inserting a screw driver blade between the valve plate and the headgear to break the pegging. The stem of any replacement valve should be scored with a rasp to give a moderately tight fit.

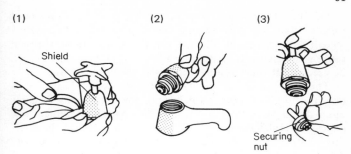

1. Turn off water supply and open tap or valve fully. Fit waste plug in sink. Wrap rag round shield and loosen it with adjustable spanner if there are flats — if not use a pipe wrench very gently. 2. Unscrew the shield fully and loosen hexagonal nut securing head using adjustable spanner. Unscrew the nut by hand and lift the head of the tap out of the body. 3. With some taps the jumper can be removed — on others it fits loosely. The washer is usually held against the jumper plate by a small nut. Some taps used a domed washer fixed to the jumper — in this case the jumper is replaced.

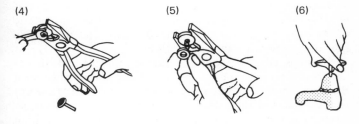

4. Grip the edge of the jumper plate with pliers and undo the nut with a small spanner. Turn the nut gently — it often gets fouled with fur and scale. If the nut cannot be removed the whole jumper will have to be replaced. Either the same type or a domed jumper (inset) can be used. 5. Remove the nut and the metal washer. The old washer is replaced by the new one, fitted with the side with the maker's name against the jumper plate. Replace the metal washer and nut and tighten securely. 6. Reassemble the head into the body as it was removed, screw down carefully by hand and tighten with the adjustable spanner. Screw down the shield — hand tight only — and turn on the water supply

Fig. 4.5. Fitting a new washer

Continued dripping after a washer has been renewed suggests that the valve seating has been scored and scratched by grit from the main. The tap can be reseated using a special tool or, alternatively, a nylon washer and valve seating kit can be used to fit a new nylon seating over the old brass one.

The way in which the head of a shrouded head tap is removed to give access to the interior for rewashering depends upon the make of the tap. Some models have a retaining screw concealed under the plastic 'Hot' or 'Cold' indicator. Prise off this plastic disc, undo the retaining screw and the head will lift off, revealing a headgear similar to that of the traditional tap. Other models have a small grub screw (resembling the grub screw retaining a crutch or capstan head) in the side of the shrouded head. The shrouded head of one of the taps in the Deltaflow range is removed by turning the tap fully on. Then the head is given a final turn and can be pulled off in the hand.

A number of taps have been produced with the object of eliminating the need to cut off the water supply before re-washering. Only one of these—the supatap—has stood the test of time. Supataps are turned on or off by turning the nozzle of the tap itself. Ears of kemetal plastic are provided to enable this to be done easily and comfortably.

Supataps are rewashered by first unscrewing and disconnecting the retaining nut at the top of the nozzle. Then open the tap and keep on turning the nozzle. At first water flow will increase but will then stop—just before the nozzle comes off in your hand—as a check valve within the tap falls into position (*Figure 4.6*). Tap the nozzle end on a hard surface—*not* the glazed surface of a ceramic sink or basin!—and turn it upside down. The anti-splash device, into which the valve and washer is fitted, will then fall out. Prise out the valve and fit a replacement. When re-assembling the tap remember that the nozzle screws in with a left hand thread. It must therefore be turned in the opposite direction from that dictated by instinct.

Leakage up the spindle of a tap when the tap is turned on indicates failure of the gland or stuffing box. It may be accompanied by water hammer—since the tap can be 'spun' on and

off much too easily—and often results from the connection of
a garden or washing machine hose having been connected to a
kitchen tap so as to produce back pressure.

*1. Hold the nozzle in one hand and loosen the gland nut with a spanner.
2. Hold the gland nut and unscrew the nozzle fully. See that the check
valve drops into position. 3. Tap the nozzle on a firm surface to loosen
the anti-splash. 4. Turn the nozzle upside down and push out the
anti-splash. 5. The jumper may be stuck in the anti-splash, but can be
gently levered out with a coin or blade*

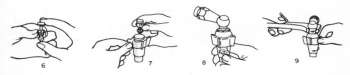

*6. Put a new jumper into the anti-splash and make sure it clicks home.
7. Drop the anti-splash into the nozzle, washer uppermost. 8. Refit the
nozzle to the tap and screw up by hand. 9. Holding the nozzle, tighten
the gland nut and ensure that the tap works properly and does not drip*

*Fig. 4.6. Replacing the washer on a Supatap. It is not necessary to turn
off the water supply to do this as a check valve does it automatically
when the tap is dismantled*

First try adjusting the gland nut. This is the first nut
through which the spindle of the tap passes. It may be possible
to reach it, without removing the tap head, by opening up the
tap fully and raising the easy-clean cover as far is it will go.
Half a turn, or a turn, in a clockwise direction may remedy
the leakage (*Figure 4.7*).

Eventually all the adjustment will be taken up and the gland
will need repacking. There is no need to cut off the water

supply to the tap to do this. Unscrew the grub screw retaining the crutch or capstan head and tap the head upwards to remove it. Remove the easy-clean cover. Unscrew and remove the gland nut and pick out all existing gland packing material with the point of a penknife blade. Repack using household wool steeped in petroleum jelly. Caulk down firmly and reassemble the tap. In some modern taps an 'O' ring seal replaces the conventional gland. It is interesting to note that

If water leaks out between the spindle and the shield the gland nut may be loose. Release the shield and tighten the nut. 1. Open the tap fully. Do not shut off the water supply. Using a small screwdriver, remove the grub screw holding the cross head on the spindle. 2. Unscrew the shield. Using an adjustable spanner, lever under the shield to force the cross head up off the spindle.

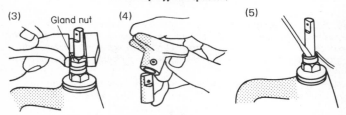

3. When the shield is removed the gland nut can be seen. Tighten the nut half a turn with the adjustable spanner. 4. Replace the cross head temporarily in order to check that the tap is easy to turn on and off. If it is too tight slacken the gland nut a little. When satisfied that the tap turns easily and does not leak reassemble the tap. 5. If the tap still leaks, shut off the water supply and remove the gland nut. Remove the packing and replace with household wool steeped in petroleum jelly. Caulk down firmly and reassemble the tap. Some modern taps have an 'O' ring seal

Fig. 4.7. Tightening a leaky gland nut

the modern shrouded head was not, in the first instance, introduced for the sake of its appearance, but in an attempt to prevent gland failure. It had been noted that housewives frequently turned taps on and off with hands dripping with household detergent. This detergent ran down the spindle of tap into the gland, from which it quickly washed the grease out of the packing.

Poor or intermittent flow, particularly from hot water taps, is more likely to be due to an air lock in the distribution pipe than to a fault in the tap itself. Air locks can usually be cured by connecting one end of a length of hose to the cold tap over the kitchen sink and the other end to the tap giving trouble. Turn both taps on and the mains pressure from the kitchen cold tap should blow the air bubble out of the system (*Figure 4.8*).

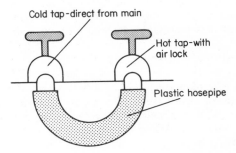

Cold tap-direct from main

Hot tap-with air lock

Plastic hosepipe

Fig. 4.8. Clearing and air lock in the hot tap over the kitchen sink — the same principle can be used in the bathroom if necessary

Constantly recurring air locks are caused by design faults that should always be investigated and remedied. The commonest single cause is too small a cold water supply pipe from the cold water storage cistern to the hot water cylinder. If this pipe is only 15mm (½in) in diameter it will be incapable of replacing hot water drawn off by a ¾in bath tap. Water level will fall in the vent pipe until air is able to enter the distribution pipe to produce a blockage.

Sometimes the supply pipe is of adequate diameter but a
gate valve of a smaller size has been fitted into it. Alternatively
a gate valve of the correct size may have been left partially
closed after a piece of maintenance has been carried out.
Other possible causes of recurring air locks are a cold water
storage cistern of inadequate capacity or one fed by a sluggish
ball valve. All 'horizontal' lengths of distribution should, in
fact, slope slightly upwards towards the cold water storage
cistern or the hot water vent pipe. This will permit any bubbles
of air that may gain access to escape.

At the time of writing taps have not yet been metricated
and are still to be found in builders merchants' catalogues
designated as ½in (for sinks, basins and bidets) and ¾in (for
baths). There is however a growing tendency to refer to them
metrically by the metric size of the copper tubing to which
they are to be connected. Thus sink and basin taps are given a
nominal size of 15mm and bath taps one of 22mm although
these dimensions represent no actual measurement of the taps
themselves.

Before fitting a pillar tap a plastic washer is slipped over
the tail of the tap to protect the surface of the fitting from
the metal base of the tap (*Figure 4.9a*). Alternatively the tap
may be bedded onto linseed oil putty or a non-setting mastic
such as the plumber's mait. Another plastic washer should be
provided under the fitting before the back nut is tightened
up. For fittings of thin materials (for example sinks and
basins of stainless or enamelled steel) a special spacer washer—
sometimes called a 'top hat' or 'cap' washer—is needed to
accommodate the protruding shank of the tap (*Figure 4.9b*).
The tail of the tap is then connected to the water supply pipe
by means of a tap connector or 'cap and liner' (*Figure 4.9c*).
This incorporates a fibre washer to ensure a watertight connection. The cap and liner may have a compression or capillary
joint outlet for connection to copper or stainless steel tubing
or a plain outlet for connection, by means of a wiped soldered
joint, to a lead supply pipe (see Chapter 12).

Bib taps are most likely to be fitted into a wall plate elbow.
The wall must be drilled and plugged and the elbow screwed to

it. Before screwing in the tail of the tap p.t.f.e. plastic thread sealing tape should be bound round the thread of the tap's tail to ensure a watertight joint.

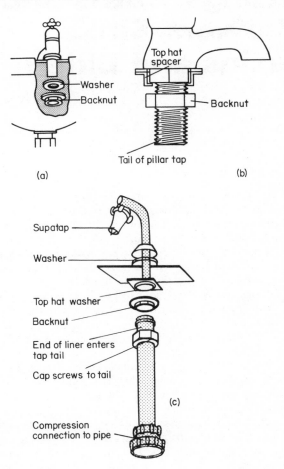

Fig. 4.9. Methods of protecting surfaces when mounting taps

5 Some Plumbing Fittings; Baths and Showers, Sinks, Basins and Bidets

Baths

Baths come in all shapes and sizes nowadays but the standard rectangular panelled bath ranging in overall size from 1500mm to 1800mm (about 5ft to 6ft) in length and from 700mm to 800mm (about 2ft 4in to 2ft 8in) in width is likely to remain the most popular choice for the average British householder.

Size will be dictated by the space available though the prudent purchaser will also bear in mind the additional fuel cost of filling one of the larger baths with warm water. Colour —and there is a wide colour range available—will depend upon the overall decor of the bathroom. It is with regard to the material of which the bath is made that the purchaser has greatest freedom of choice.

The traditional material is enamelled cast iron (*Figure 5.1*). Any bath installed more than twenty to twenty five years ago will certainly be of this material. The fact that there are still so many of them installed and in regular use is a tribute to their strength and toughness. They have disadvantages though. They are extremely heavy. Installing (or removing) one is certainly not a one man job. The thick iron of which they are made tends to conduct away heat, quickly cooling the water run into them. Once the enamelled surface is damaged renovation can be extremely difficult, if not impossible, and corrosion can attack the metal underneath. They are also, by most people's standards, very expensive.

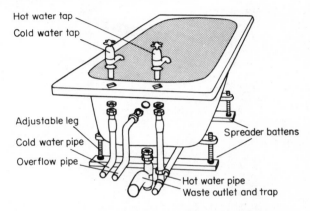

Hot water tap
Cold water tap
Adjustable leg
Cold water pipe
Overflow pipe
Spreader battens
Hot water pipe
Waste outlet and trap

Fig. 5.1. Detail of enamelled cast iron bath with lead water supply pipes

For all of these reasons the cheaper, lighter and more easily installed enamelled pressed steel bath enjoys considerable popularity. A disadvantage is its liability to accidental damage in storage, transport or installation. To overcome this objection, one bath manufacturer (the Curran Engineering Co. Ltd.) has produced a 'supersteel' bath, backed by guarantee, made of 2.5mm gauge steel. This is 50% thicker than that used for standard enamel steel baths but baths made of this material are still only half the weight of cast iron baths of the same size.

The third material of which baths may be made is acrylic plastic. These baths show a steady increase in popularity and offer many advantages to the householder and to the professional or d.i.y. installer. Tough and hard wearing, they are also extremely light in weight and easy to handle. It is well within the capacity of one man to unload one from the

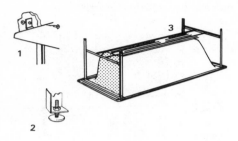

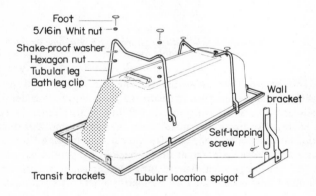

Fig. 5.2. Cradles for acrylic baths. A universal wall fixing bracket (1) may be used at the side, or over the lip, of the bath. Screw adjustments (2) at five points will allow for uneven floors. Metal cradles as at (3) can be assembled allowing for support for the bath and for fixing side panels

delivery vehicle, carry it upstairs to the bathroom and install it single-handed. They are available in a wide range of colours and the colour extends throughout the material. Small surface scratches can be polished out without trace. Acrylic plastic has good insulating properties retaining the heat of the bath water and remaining comfortable to the touch. It is possible to purchase acrylic plastic baths with a flat, non-slip, base that eliminates a frequent cause of home accidents among the elderly.

Acrylic plastic baths are supplied with strong metal or wooden frames and cradles (*Figure 5.2*) that should be assembled and secured to wall and floor exactly as indicated in the instructions of the manufacturer. Felt padding is provided at points of contact. These padded cradles eliminate the sagging and creaking when filled that occurred with early models of this kind of bath.

Acrylic plastic can be permanently damaged by extreme heat. When working with a blow torch in a bathroom fitted with a bath of this material keep the blow torch flame well away from the bath. Similarly the householder should make sure that all members of his family, and visitors, are made aware that placing a lighted cigarette, even briefly, on the bath rim, can cause irreparable damage.

When fitting a bath of any kind the cramped space available at the end of the bath should be borne in mind. Carry out as much of the plumbing work as possible before moving the bath into position. Fit the taps or mixer as described in the previous chapter and bed down the waste outlet in non-setting mastic, tightening up the back nut beneath the bath. Have the hot and cold water supply pipes in position with their tap connectors fitted. The trap should be connected to the waste pipe with its flexible overflow pipe ready for connection to the bath overflow. It is wise to use a plastic trap and waste pipe with an acrylic bath. There will be some movement as the bath fills with hot water and a rigid metal trap and waste pipe could cause damage.

Having moved the bath into position, make the plumbing connections in logical order so as to make the most of the limited space available. First connect the trap to the waste outlet (*Figure 5.3*). Then connect the further tap to its supply pipe. Next make the overflow connection and finally the

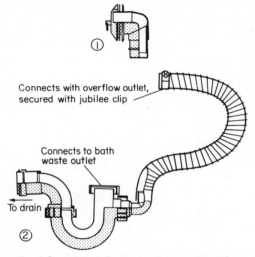

Connects with overflow outlet, secured with jubilee clip

Connects to bath waste outlet

To drain

Fig. 5.3. Bath overflow (1) and waste (2) outlets

connection of the supply pipe to the nearer tap. All that will then remain is to fit the bath panels and to fill the gap between the side of the bath and the wall with a suitable mastic filler.

Showers

A shower may be provided either in connection with a conventional sit-down bath or as a separate facility in its own shower cabinet. There can be few people nowadays who are unaware of the advantages that a shower has to offer. They save both time and money. Five or six showers can be taken with the same amount of hot water—and in scarcely more time—than would be required for one sit-down bath. They are more hygienic and mean less work for the housewife clearing up afterwards. A shower cubicle will be easier and safer for an elderly or disabled person to enter than a sit-down bath.

Where a house is being converted into self-contained flats an independent shower can be provided in any space, on a landing, in a hallway or even under the stairs, where there is a space at least 3ft square. 'A fixed bath *or shower*' is one of the amenities for the provision of which the owner of an older house can claim an improvement grant from his local council.

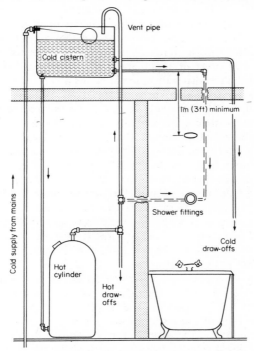

Fig. 5.4. Design requirements of a shower installation

A shower can usually be provided without difficulty in any home with a cylinder storage hot water system. There are however certain, quite specific, design requirements that must be met.

The first is that to ensure safe and efficient mixing, the hot and cold water supplies to the shower must be under equal pressure. With a cylinder storage system the hot water supply will be under pressure from the main cold water storage cistern. The cold supply must therefore also be taken from this cistern (*Figure 5.4*).

It is illegal, and impracticable, to connect the hot side of a shower to a hot water supply from a cistern and storage cylinder and to connect the cold side to the rising main. Pressure must be adequate. This depends upon the height of the cold water storage cistern above the shower sprinkler. Best results will be obtained if the base of this cistern is 5ft (about 1500mm) or more above the sprinkler. However if pipe runs are short with minimal bends a vertical distance of 3ft (about 900mm) may be sufficient.

Finally, the cold supply to the shower should be taken in a separate distribution pipe direct from the storage cistern, not as a branch from some other cold water distribution pipe. This is a safety precaution. If the shower cold supply is taken as a branch from another distribution pipe, flushing a w.c. cistern or running a basin cold tap could reduce pressure on the cold side of the shower. Pressure on the hot side would remain constant and serious scalding could result.

The design of some hot and cold water supply systems may make it impossible to comply with all of these requirements. Nevertheless there can be few homes in which it is absolutely impossible to install a shower.

Where the cold water storage cistern is not sufficiently high above the shower sprinkler to provide the minimum 3ft (900mm) head of pressure the simplest solution is usually to raise the level of the cistern. This may involve moving it from the upper part of an airing cupboard into the roof space or constructing a wooden platofrm for it above the roof timbers. This cannot be done where there is a 'packaged plumbing system' (see Chapter 3) in which the cold water storage cistern and the hot water cylinder comprise one unit. It may be impossible too in flats and ground floor maisonettes where there is no access to the roof space. There are however available

electrically operated shower pumps which will effectively
boost pressure to the shower sprinkler (*Figure 5.5*). These
operate on a flow switch and are brought into action when
the control valve of the shower is turned on. They do, of
course, make an appreciable addition to the cost of the
installation.

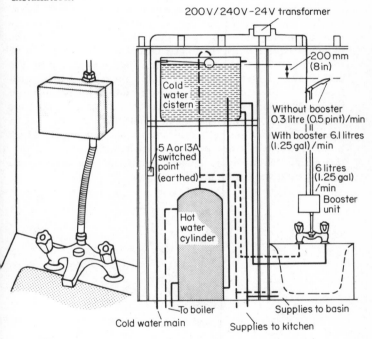

Fig. 5.5. Installing a shower using a booster unit

Where bathroom cold supplies are direct from the main it
will be possible, in many cases, to bring the cold supply to the
shower from the cistern supplying the hot water cylinder. In
some instances though this will have too small a capacity to
do more than supply the hot water system. In others, where
all hot and cold water supplies are direct from the main,

there may be no storage cistern at all. It is under these circumstances that the instantaneous electric shower units that
have been developed in recent years can prove invaluable.
They need only connection to a mains water supply and a
suitable source of electric power to provide an 'instant
shower'.

Apart from electric instantaneous showers, which incorporate their own control valve, all showers need to have some
kind of mixing valve to blend the hot and cold water to the
bather's requirements. The bath taps themselves can provide
the simplest kind of shower mixer. They may comprise the
bath/shower mixer referred to in the previous chapter with
facility for diverting the flow of water into the bath or up to
the shower sprinkler at the flick of a switch. A portable
rubber shower, with push-on tap connectors, can be used to
convert any pair of bath taps into a shower mixer. These
basic shower kits work perfectly satisfactorily provided that
the design requirements already mentioned are met by the
hot and cold water systems of the house.

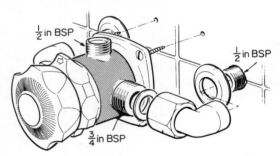

Fig. 5.6. Fixing a manual mixing valve

It usually takes considerable adjustment, and some dis-
comfort, before a 'mixing valve' of this kind produces a stream
of water at exactly the temperature required. Better control is
achieved with a single unit 'manual shower mixing valve'
(*Figure 5.6*) which gives control of the shower temperature
and, in some instances, flow control as well, by turning a

single control knob. Manual mixers of this kind are installed in most independent shower cabinets and there are over-bath versions available too.

Finally there is the 'thermostatic shower mixing valve' which is capable of dealing with fluctuations of pressure in the hot or cold supply pipes and providing a mix of constant temperature. These valves are naturally more expensive. They are particularly useful in hotels, schools and similar institutions where a number of showers are run from single hot and cold water distributing pipes. They are also of value in domestic situations where providing *separate* distribution pipes from the cold water storage cistern to the shower presents difficulties. Early thermostatic mixing valves needed a considerable head of pressure, perhaps as much as 10ft (3m), to work effectively. There are however present day models that will operate satisfactorily on the minimal 3ft (900mm) head required by a manual mixing valve.

It should be realised that a thermostatic valve cannot increase pressure on either the hot or the cold supply. It can only reduce the pressure on one side to match that on the other. If therefore, cold water pressure is reduced to a thermostatic valve already operating on minimal head, the shower will simply dry up until pressure is restored.

A shower fitted over a bath needs some means of preventing water from splashing onto the bathroom floor. Plastic shower curtains provide the cheapest means of doing this but glass panels, which may be hinged or detachable, provide a neater and more professional solution. Shower trays may be of ceramic material, of acrylic plastic or of enamelled steel. Waste and trap are fitted and connected to the branch waste pipe in the same way as are those of a bath except that shower trays are not normally fitted with an overflow.

Sinks

Houses built between about 1920 and 1950 were almost invariably fitted with glazed fireclay, 'Belfast pattern', sinks

(*Figure 5.7a*). These were supported by heavy iron cantilever brackets built into the wall. They had a built-in weir overflow and a separate, hook-on, wooden draining board. Water supply was from bib-taps protruding from the tiled wall surface behind the sink. These sinks have been superseded, for

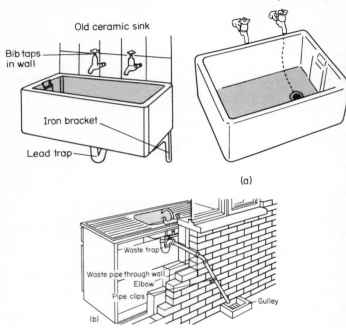

Fig. 5.7. Kitchen sinks. The 'Belfast' pattern ceramic glazed sink (a) is usually mounted on iron brackets fixed to the wall; these must be removed or cut back when replacing with a modern sink. The modern sink unit (b) is fairly simple to fit

both new and replacement work, by sink units with a stainless steel or enamelled pressed steel sink and integral drainer (*Figure 5.7b*). Sinks of either of these materials are more attractive in appearance, more easily cleaned and less damaging to accidentally dropped crockery than those of glazed fireclay.

Enamelled steel sinks are available in a number of colours but suffer from the disadvantage that the enamel is liable to accidental damage. For this reason a stainless steel sink is the modern housewife's most usual choice.

Stainless steel sinks designed for sink unit installation are provided with tap holes to take pillar taps or a sink mixer. They may have a built-in overflow but are nowadays more likely to have an overflow hole only provided. The overflow pipe is intended to be a flexible one fitted into the trap in the same way as the overflow of a modern bath (*Figure 5.8*).

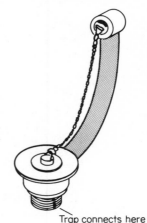

*Fig. 5.8. Sink waste incor-
porating overflow pipe*

Trap connects here

Since both stainless steel and enamelled pressed steel are thin materials a spacer or top-hat washer (see previous chapter) must be slipped over the tail of each tap before the back-nut is screwed home. When installing a new sink unit the taps should be fitted before the unit is placed in position. Waste, trap and overflow are fitted as for a bath. Where the unit has a double sink a trap is fitted only under one outlet—the one nearer to the waste pipe. The waste from the other section of the sink is taken untrapped to connect above trap level.

If a sink waste disposal unit (*Figure 5.9*) is to be fitted the sink must have a 3½in (87.5mm) waste hole instead of the standard 1½in (38mm) hole. The waste holes of stainless steel, but not enamelled steel, sinks can be enlarged to this size with a tool obtainable from the supplier of the unit. Waste

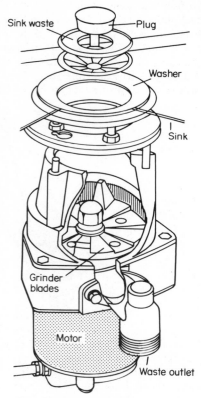

Fig. 5.9. Sink waste disposal unit (garbage grinder). The unit is easy to fit, but an electrician should be employed if new wiring is necessary

disposal units are fitted by placing a rubber or plastic washer round the outlet hole and inserting the flange of the unit. The unit is then connected beneath the sink by means of a snap fastening. The outlet of the disposal unit connects to a trap in the usual way. Waste disposal units are operated by an electric motor and will grind soft household and kitchen waste to a slurry that can then be flushed into the drain by running the cold tap.

Basins

Although wash basins, or lavatory basins as they are referred to in builders merchants' catalogues, may be made of enamelled pressed steel or of plastic materials the traditional ceramic basin retains its popularity and is the kind most likely to be chosen for new or replacement work.

Ceramic basins may be either wall hung or pedestal in design. Pedestal basins are often preferred for bathroom use because of their appearance and their capacity for concealing water supply and waste pipes. Modern pedestal basins are always provided with concealed hangers or wall brackets to help support the basin's weight.

The height of a pedestal basin is, of course, decided by the pedestal. Wall-hung basins may be fitted at any height convenient to the user. Since one bends over a basin to wash it should be set at a lower level than the kitchen sink—32in (about 81cm) from floor level to rim is usual. Particularly with wall-hung basins it is important to check that the wall is capable of supporting the weight of the basin and someone leaning on it. Breeze partitions offer a somewhat dubious support and it is wise to use a pedestal basin in such a position.

Taps, or a basin mixer, are fitted in the same way as they are in a sink unit. The thicker material of a ceramic basin makes it possible to use a flat plastic (instead of a top-hat) washer between the back-nut and the material of the basin. Do not overtighten the back-nut. Ceramic basins are very easily damaged in installation. Basins of this kind have a built-in or 'secret' overflow (*Figure 5.10*). The waste fitting must therefore incorporate an overflow slot. When this fitting is bedded down into the waste outlet, care must be taken to ensure

that the overflow slot coincides with the outlet of the built-in
overflow. The basin must, of course, have a trapped outlet.
Chromium plated brass or plastic bottle traps are space saving
and neat in appearance. They can be obtained with adjustable
inlets that permit easy connection to an existing waste pipe in
replacement work.

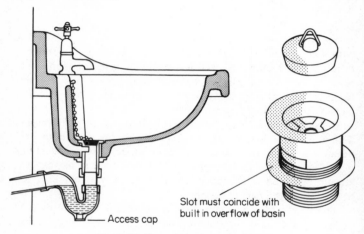

Fig. 5.10. Ceramic basin waste fittings

(a)   (b)

Fig. 5.11. Vanity units fitted (a) in the bathroom, (b) in a bedroom

Enamelled steel or plastic wash basins are usually inset into
a toilet table to form a 'vanity unit'. Such a unit may be
installed in either a bathroom or a bedroom (*Figure 5.11*).

In the latter situation they constitute an extremely attractive, and useful, piece of bedroom furniture. A vanity unit may be regarded as the ablutionary equivalent of a sink unit. Apart from the cold water supply—which will normally come from a storage cistern and not from the main—it is plumbed in in exactly the same way. Hot water supply to the wash basin will probably be taken from the household domestic hot water system. However, where the basin is used for hand washing only and is remote from other plumbing fittings, the provision of an instantaneous electric water heater providing a spray for hand washing can be an economy. A heater of this kind can be very useful for a basin in a cloakroom or w.c. compartment used only occasionally.

Bidets

Bidets are specially shaped, low level, wash basins designed for cleansing the lower parts of the body. Virtually unknown in the United Kingdom prior to World War II they are gradually gaining acceptance in this country. It may well be that the well-appointed bathroom of the future will contain a shower cubicle, a wash basin and a bidet rather than, as at present, a wash basin and sit down bath.

There are two, quite different, designs of bidet. The differences between them result in differences in means of installation that should be clearly understood by both the plumber and the householder. In an identical situation the cost of installing one pattern of bidet is likely to be considerably greater than that of installing the other.

The simpler pattern, which is cheaper both to purchase and to install, is usually described as an 'over rim supply' bidet. Apart from its shape it is identical to a bathroom wash basin. Holes are provided for pillar taps or, more probably, a pillar mixer. There may be a pop-up waste or an ordinary chain secured waste plug. The bidet is filled with warm water before use in the same way as a wash basin. Bidets of this kind can be plumbed into existing bathroom hot and cold water supplies without any special precautions being taken. If there are 22mm (¾in) hot and cold distribution pipes supplying ¾in bath hot and cold taps, reducing tee junctions 22mm to 15mm may be inserted into these distributing pipes and taken to the bidet taps or mixer.

The other type of bidet is described as 'rim supply with ascending douche'. This has a rim not unlike the flushing rim of a w.c. pan and a douche directing a spray of warm water to those parts of the body to be cleansed (*Figure 5.12*). Warm water flows into the bidet via the flushing rim which it thereby warms and makes comfortable for use. When required the water flow can be diverted to the ascending douche.

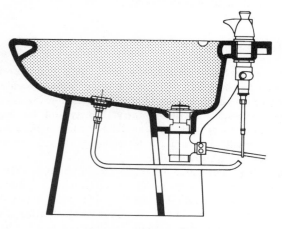

Fig. 5.12. Section through a rim supply bidet

It is the ascending douche, with its outlet below normal water level, that complicates plumbing installation. With any water inlet of this kind precautions have to be taken to ensure that other water supplies, especially mains water supplies, cannot be contaminated by accidental back-siphonage. The purpose for which the bidet is used makes this particularly important in this case.

To avoid this danger the hot and cold supplies to a 'rim supply with ascending douche' bidet must *not* be taken as branch supplies from pipes supplying any other draw-off point. They must be taken, as separate distribution pipes,

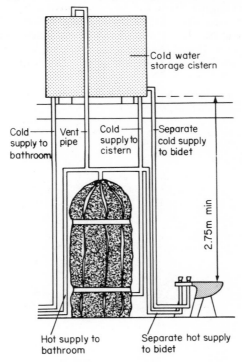

Fig. 5.13. Design requirements for a rim supply bidet

direct from the hot water storage cylinder and the cold water storage cistern (*Figure 5.13*). As a further precaution the base of the cold water storage cistern should be at least 2745mm (9ft) above the level of the bidet inlet.

Where there is a two-pipe drainage system (see Chapter 7) a distinction is made between 'soil' and 'waste' fittings. 'Soil appliances' such as w.c.s are connected directly to the drain or soil pipe. 'Waste appliances'—baths, sinks and basins—are disconnected from the drain by means of a gully.

Plumbers sometimes argue that, because of the nature of the use of bidet, it should be regarded as a 'soil appliance' and connected direct to the drain. This is incorrect. A bidet is a waste or ablutionary appliance and, where a two-pipe drainage system is installed, it should be disconnected from the drain in the same way as other waste and ablutionary fittings.

6 The W.C. Suite

From many points of view the w.c. suite is the most important and critical item of the householder's plumbing installation. A bad choice of suite can lead to embarrassment. Faulty installation can produce a positive risk to health.

It is not always realised that there are three different kinds of w.c. suite in common use, and they they depend upon quite different principles for their cleaning and recharging with water after use.

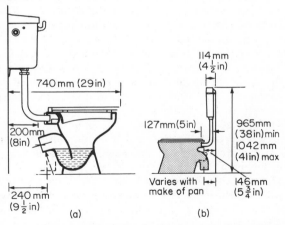

Fig. 6.1. Conventional low-level suite (a) and low-level suite with flush panel (b). Both types are wash-down pans

Commonest (and cheapest) is the straightforward wash-down suite (*Figure 6.1*). This depends for its flushing and cleansing action solely upon the weight and momentum of the two gallons of water released when the flushing cistern is discharged. Wash-down w.c. pans may be used in both high level and low level suites. For efficient cleansing—particularly with low level suites—the following conditions are essential.

(a) The float arm of the ball-valve should be adjusted so that the water level of the cistern when full is at the mark indicated on the inside of the cistern wall, usually about ½in below the overflow of warning outlet.

(b) The flush pipe (often called a 'flush bend' with a low level suite) should be of the diameter and length recommended by the manufacturer. It is best (though not absolutely essential) when installing a low level suite to buy pan, flush bend and cistern as one unit from the supplier.

(c) The flush pipe must connect absolutely squarely to the flushing horn of the w.c. pan and no jointing material must be permitted to obstruct the flush inlet. The old-fashioned way of connecting a flush pipe to a w.c. pan was with a 'rag and putty joint'. Apart from the fact that a connection of this kind is thoroughly unhygienic, the nature of the joint frequently resulted in putty obstructing the flush. Some modern w.c. pans are provided with a patent 'O' ring connector for the flush pipe. The alternative is to use a push-on rubber cone connector.

(d) There must be no obstruction—from putty, flakes of rust, hard water scale or other debris—within either side of the flushing rim. This can be checked with a mirror or by feeling with the fingers.

(e) The pan must be set dead level. This should be checked with a spirit level. If necessary, the pan can be made level by packing slivers of wood, or pieces of linoleum, under the lower side.

(f) The pan outlet must be set squarely into the socket of the branch drain or soil-pipe and, when fitting, care must be taken to ensure that any cement or mastic jointing material is not extruded into the connection between pan and socket to reduce its effective diameter.

When a wash-down suite is properly installed flushing water should flow evenly from each side of the flushing rim, the flushing water should meet in the middle of the front of the pan and there should be no marked rise in water level and no 'whirl-pool effect' as the pan empties.

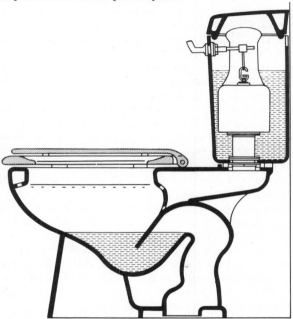

Fig. 6.2. The single-trap siphonic suite (close coupled). At the start of the flush water rises in the bowl and then rapidly discharges over the weir of the trap. This completely changes the upper portion of the trappage drawing air with it and a strong siphonic action is created

Wash-down suites are suitable for most domestic, industrial and commercial purposes. Where a more positive cleansing action is required or where the position of the w.c. suite (a compartment just inside the front door of a house or immediately outside an executive office suite, for instance) makes silent, unobtrusive action a prime consideration, then one or other of the two kinds of siphonic w.c. suite should be installed. These depend, to a greater or less extent, upon the weight of the atmosphere to push out the contents of the pan by siphonic action. Since they do not depend upon the weight and momentum of the flushing water for their cleansing effect they permit the use of 'close coupled' w.c. suites in which the flushing cistern and the pan comprise one unit without even the short 'flush bend' required for a low level wash-down suite. This markedly reduces the noise of flushing.

The simpler 'single trap' siphonic suite depends for its effectiveness upon the design of the outlet of the pan (*Figure 6.2*). Immediately behind the trap the outlet is first constricted and then widened. When the flush is operated, water overflowing from the trap completely fills the constricted section of the outlet and then enters the wider section carrying air with it. This creates the partial vacuum upon which siphonic action depends and the contents of the pan are pushed out by atmospheric pressure.

When a siphonic closet of this type is flushed water will first rise slightly in the pan. The contents will then be quite forcibly ejected. The siphonic action will cease when water level within the pan falls to a level at which air can pass into the trap. Single trap siphonic suites are rather prone to accidental blockage—usually as a result of misuse. Although they flush silently the passage of air into the trap to break the siphon can produce a somewhat noisy gurgle.

A more positively silent action is provided by the double-trap siphonic w.c. suite. A suite of this kind is, in my opinion, always to be preferred where silent, unobtrusive and efficient action is of greater importance than the initial cost of installation.

As its name implies a double trap siphonic suite has two traps built into the outlet (*Figure 6.3*). The air space between the two traps is connected to the flushing inlet by means of a short pipe or 'pressure reducing device'. When the flush is operated, water flowing over this pressure reducing device aspirates air from the air space in the same way that the wind,

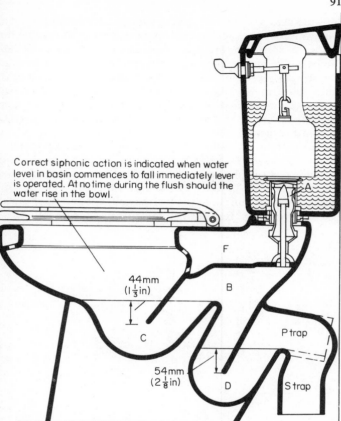

Correct siphonic action is indicated when water level in basin commences to fall immediately lever is operated. At no time during the flush should the water rise in the bowl.

Figure 6.3. The double-trap (close coupled) siphonic suite. Water flowing down the leg of the siphon passes through the pressure-reducing fitment A. This lowers the air pressure in chamber B and a powerful siphonic action is set up which draws the contents of the basin through sealed traps C and D into the soil pipe. Simultaneously the sides of the bowl are thoroughly washed by streams of water from the perforated rim E. After flushing, complete resealing of the two traps is ensured by after-flush chamber F.

Correct siphonic action is indicated when the water level in the basin starts to fall immediately the lever is operated. At no time during the flush should the water rise in the basin blowing across a chimney stack, will aspirate air up the flue from the room below. This action creates a partial vacuum in the space between the two traps and the pressure of the atmospheric pushes out the contents of the pan. Where a double-trap siphonic suite has been properly installed the water level in the pan can be seen to fall *before* flushing water actually reaches the pan. Having set the siphonic action into operation the main purpose of the flushing water is merely to recharge the pan.

Apart from its silent action a further advantage of this kind of w.c. suite is the fact that the large water area that its design makes possible, reduces the risk of the sides of the pan becoming fouled. Unlike most sanitary appliances the trap of the w.c. suite is built in to the fitting itself. Ground floor w.c.s usually have an 'S' trap with an outlet connected directly to a

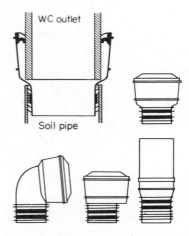

Fig. 6.4. Push on plastic w.c. connectors

branch underground drain. Upstairs w.c.s are usually connected to a branch soil pipe and have a 'P' trap with a horizontal outlet. A variety of angled 'P' outlets are available for installation in difficult situations.

It is usual nowadays to connect both ground floor and upstairs w.c.s to the drain or soil pipe by means of some kind of flexible joint (*Figure 6.4*). This may be a patent push-on plastic joint such as the 'multikwik' or may be made in situ using a non-setting mastic filler such as 'plumber's mait'.

In the past ground floor w.c.s were always connected to the stoneware drain socket by means of a cement and sand joint using two parts of cement to one of sand. A grommet of tarred hemp, or a wad of dampened newspaper, was first caulked into the space between pan outlet and socket to prevent jointing material entering the drain and causing a partial obstruction. Upstairs w.c.s were sometimes connected to iron branch soil pipe sockets in the same way. This was never a satisfactory arrangement however. Vibration or movement of the wooden floor to which the w.c. pan was screwed inevitably resulted in a cracked and leaking joint.

Remedying a leak in the joint between w.c. outlet and drain or soil-pipe socket is a common maintenance job. A radical remedy is, of course, to disconnect the w.c. pan and to replace the existing joint with a push-on plastic one. This may not be convenient or even possible. An alternative is to rake out the existing jointing material and to bind two or three turns of a waterproofing building tape such as 'sylglas' round the w.c. outlet, caulking it down hard into the socket of the soil pipe or drain. Fill in the space between outlet and socket with a non-setting mastic such as 'plumber's mait' and complete the joint with another couple of turns of waterproofing tape.

When fitting a new w.c. pan onto a solid floor it should *not*—as was usual in the past—be set in a bed of sand and cement mix. It has been established that the setting of the cement can produce damaging stresses. The pan should be screwed down with non-corroding screws. Place the pan in position. Mark through the screw holes with a ball-point refill. Remove the pan, drill the floor and plug. In order to make sure that the pan is placed in exactly the correct position over the plugs it is a good idea to insert short pieces of wire (straightened out paper clips will do) into the plugs. The pan can then be lowered over these pieces of wire which are removed before the screws are inserted. Slip a lead washer over each screw before insertion to avoid the risk of damaging the ceramic surface of the w.c. pan.

Although direct-action flat bottomed flushing cisterns are in universal use for new and replacement work there are still many thousands of the older Burlington or 'bell' high level cisterns in use, particularly in external w.c. compartments in older properties (*Figure 6.5*). Their function and failings

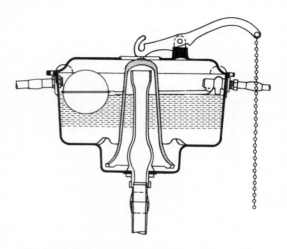

Fig. 6.5. Bell pattern well-bottomed flushing cistern

should be clearly understood. Burlington pattern cisterns are invariably made of iron. Their essential feature is a well in the base in which stands a heavy iron bell. A stand-pipe connects to the flush pipe and rises, within the bell, to terminate open-ended an inch or so above 'full' water level. The bell has lugs cast into its base to permit water to pass freely.

To operate the flush the bell is raised, usually by means of a chain, and is then suddenly released. Its weight causes it to fall rapidly back into the well of the cistern and its conical shape forces the water trapped inside it up and over the lip of the stand-pipe. This water, falling down the stand-pipe into the flush-pipe, carries air with it thus creating the partial vacuum upon which siphonic action depends. Atmospheric pressure then pushes the water in the cistern under the base of the bell and into the flush-pipe to flush the w.c. The siphon is broken when water level falls to the base of the bell and air can enter.

Burlington cisterns are always noisy in operation. There is the clank of the descending bell, the rush of water from high level and the gurgle as the siphon is broken. Since they are usually connected directly to the main refilling, under mains pressure, is also noisy.

Another fault to which Burlington cisterns are prone, particularly after they have been in use (as most of them have) for many years, is continuing siphonage. After the cistern has been flushed the siphon fails to break. Water continues to flow into the cistern through the ball-valve and there is a continuous flow down the flush-pipe that can be stopped only by 'pulling the chain' again at the end of the operation. A number of circumstances contribute to the this failing. After years of use the lugs at the base of the bell become worn, reducing the gap between the base of the bell and that of the well. Rust from inside the cistern and grit and debris from the water main accumulate in the well, further reducing the space through which air must pass in order to break the siphon. Coupled with a high water pressure and an efficient ball valve these two factors result in the rim of the well being continuously covered with water. The siphon can be broken only by pulling the chain and raising the bell again.

This trouble can usually be cured by the simple expedient of cleaning the rust and debris out of the well. In some cases it may be necessary, by turning down the stop-cock on the water supply to the cistern, to reduce the flow of water through the ball-valve. In others it may be possible to 'build up' the lugs on the base of the well with an epoxy resin filler such as 'plastic padding' or 'isopon', or to drill a hole through the metal of the bell an inch or so above its base to permit air to enter. A better solution is, of course, the more radical one of replacing the old and obsolete cistern with a modern 'direct action' one.

Direct action cisterns normally have a flat base though there are well-bottomed models available to facilitate the replacement of old bell pattern cisterns with the minimum of alteration to the plumbing. Like bell pattern cisterns, direct action ones have a stand-pipe connected to the flush-pipe that rises from the base of the cistern to a point an inch or so above

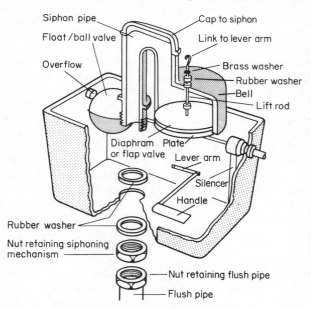

Fig. 6.6. Direct action flushing cistern

water level. This stand-pipe is not however open-ended at this point. It is bent over in an inverted U and widened to form a dome with an open base extending almost to the bottom of the cistern (*Figure 6.6*). A rod connected by a metal link to the flushing handle passes through the dome to connect to the centre of a circular metal plate. The metal plate has a hole, or holes, in it to permit water to pass freely upwards but a kind of non-return valve, usually a plastic disc, closes these holes when the plate is raised.

These cisterns are often loosely referred to as 'low level cisterns' though they may, of course, be installed at low level, at high level or as part of a close-coupled suite. High level cisterns of this kind are operated by pulling a chain in the same way as a Burlington pattern cistern. Flushing takes place as the chain is pulled not, as with a Burlington cistern, when it is released. The most usual method of operating a low level direct action cistern is by depressing a lever. However press button operation is becoming increasingly popular and there are also pedal operated models on the market. These are particularly to be commended in commercial food premises where every means by which the operatives can avoid con-tamination of the hands should be encouraged.

Whatever the means adopted to induce flushing the action within the cistern is the same. The metal plate within the dome of the siphon is raised throwing water over the inverted U into the flush pipe. This falling water carries air with its to create a partial vacuum thus inducing siphonic action. Once siphonic action has begun water flow raises the plastic diaphragm or 'flap valve' on the plate to permit water to pass through freely.

Failure of this plastic diaphragm is the commonest fault encountered in direct action cisterns. The user finds that, whereas originally the cistern flushed promptly at the first attempt, several sharp jerks are necessary to induce siphonic action. The diaphragm is no longer blocking the holes in the plate and, when the plate is raised, water passes back into the cistern instead of being thrown over into the flush pipe.

To renew the diaphragm the flushing siphon must be removed from the cistern. First of all, tie up the arm of the ball-valve to prevent water from flowing in and flush to empty. Next unscrew the nut securing the external flush pipe to the threaded tail of the siphoning mechanism protruding from the cistern's base. Disconnect the flush pipe. With some makes of cistern the siphoning mechanism is secured by bolts within the cistern itself. In most cases however the siphon can be withdrawn after unscrewing and removing the large nut immediately below the cistern's base. As you loosen this nut the pint or so of water remaining after flushing will be released. Be prepared for this!

Once the siphon has been withdrawn the plate can be removed after disconnecting it from the 'link' connection with the flushing handle. It is important that the replacement diaphragm should be of the correct size. This will normally be purchased before the cistern is dismantled. If in doubt about the size required choose the largest—it can easily be cut to size with a pair of scissors. The diaphragm should overlap the plate and touch, but not drag on, the walls of the siphon dome.

Slow refilling is another fault that may be encountered with any kind of flushing cistern. After flushing the cistern should refill and be ready for use within two minutes. Failure to refill promptly is usually the result of the cistern being fitted with a high pressure ball valve where a low pressure or fullway model is required. Cisterns fed direct from the main normally require a high pressure valve. A cistern supplied from a roof storage cistern will probably fill sufficiently quickly if a low pressure valve is installed. Where the storage cistern is below roof level, perhaps in an airing cupboard only a few feet above the level of the flushing cistern, a full-way valve may well be needed.

If a valve of the correct type has been installed slow filling is almost certainly the result of the valve jamming because of an accumulation of hard water scale. The valve should be dismantled and cleaned as suggested in Chapter 2.

Condensation is another trouble to which all w.c. flushing cisterns are prone. Iron Burlington pattern cisterns may be treated with two or more coats of an insulating anti-condensation paint but this treatment cannot be used to prevent condensation on the external surfaces of modern plastic or ceramic cisterns. As with all condensation problems the best remedy lies in warmth and ventilation. Consideration should be given to the provision of a radiant heat source directed towards the cistern and to improved means of ventilation, perhaps an electric extractor fan fitted into the window of the w.c. compartment.

It is worth bearing in mind that plastic cisterns, being of a self-insulating material, are less subject to condensation than ceramic ones. Cisterns supplied from the marginally warmer water of a cold water storage cistern are also less prone to condensation than those supplied direct from the main.

Bathroom w.c.s are more likely to have condensation troubles than w.c.s installed in a separate compartment. Here there are one or two steps that can be taken to reduce this nuisance. Refrain from drip-drying clothing over the bath. Always run one or two inches of cold water into the bath before turning on the hot tap. It may even be worth connecting a length of rubber tubing to the bath hot tap so that incoming water enters below the level of water already in the bath.

As a last resort consider insulating the inside of the cistern. Empty the cistern and dry it thoroughly. Then apply strips of expanded polystyrene wall paper lining to the interior of the cistern using an epoxy resin adhesive such as Araldite to retain the lining in position. Do not refill until the adhesive has set.

Finally there is the problem of noise. A w.c. that makes its presence known by its noise is a source of annoyance and embarrassment to the householder. Noise may arise from the cistern refilling, from the flush itself or from the contents of the w.c. flushing into the soil pipe. Noisy refilling depends upon the ball-valve and has been dealt with in Chapter 2. So far as the noise of the flush is concerned it should be remembered that a low level suite is more silent in action than a high level one and that a close coupled suite—particularly if it is a double trap siphonic one—is the most silent of all.

The connection between w.c. outlet and soil pipe should always be of mastic or plastic material that does not readily transmit sound. In some cases it may help if a hard rubber pad is interposed between the base of the w.c. pan and the floor or if dry sand, or a layer of vermiculite chips, is run onto the ceiling of the room immediately below the w.c.

Attempts to silence a noisy w.c. are rarely *wholly* satisfactory. For reasons that lie within the province of a psychologist rather than a plumber, once a householder has become aware of a nuisance from noise the volume of the noise can be reduced many times but, to the hearer, will remain a source of annoyance.

For this reason it is important that the installer should foresee, and forestall, this problem before or during installation.

7 Above-ground Drainage

Leaky and insanitary drainage systems, coupled with equally unsatisfactory sources of water supply, were directly responsible for the epidemics of typhoid fever and cholera with which Britain was plagued until towards the end of the nineteenth century.

Victorian sanitary and social reformers noted the coincidence of bad drainage and disease but, lacking modern knowledge of the means of spread of infection, they drew the wrong conclusions. They became obsessed with the idea that bad drains were responsible for all the ills to which the flesh is heir. Not only the diseases already mentioned were attributed to this cause but such unlikely candidates as diphtheria, scarlet fever, smallpox and tuberculosis were blamed upon the malign influence of 'drain air'.

The results of this misapprehension were almost wholly beneficial. The provision of watertight, self-cleansing drainage systems prevented the contamination of water supplies and water-borne cholera and typhoid were virtually eliminated. Improved domestic ventilation—intended to get rid of 'drain smells'—did something to reduce the incidence of air-borne droplet infections such as scarlet fever and diphtheria.

However, their determination to 'keep drain smells out of the home' resulted in the cumbersome and obsolescent 'two pipe' system of drainage which remained with us until well on into the 1960s. It is, in fact, only in the last few years that the modern 'single stack' drainage system has ceased to be regarded with suspicion by at least some plumbers and environmental

101

health engineers. The purpose of the two-pipe system was to keep as much of the drainage system as possible outside the walls of the house. Barriers were interposed to remove the least possibility of gases from the drain or sewer entering the home. Since the majority of houses in this country were built prior to the 1960s, the two-pipe system of drainage is the one most likely to be encountered in existing buildings (*Figure 7.1*).

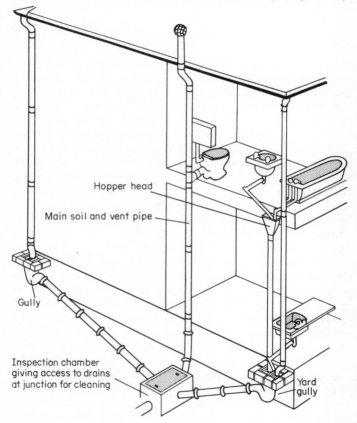

Fig. 7.1. Two-pipe drainage system

The two-pipe system makes a firm distinction between 'soil' and 'waste' appliances. W.c.s, urinals and slop-sinks are soil appliances although, of course, only the first of these is likely to be found in the home. Soil appliances could be connected directly to the drainage system. The trap built into the appliance afforded a barrier against 'drain air'. A further precaution is that the w.c. compartment must be adequately ventilated—by means of a window opening to the external air or by mechanical means ensuring at least three air changes per hour. Furthermore there must be an 'intervening ventilated space' between the w.c. compartment and any room used for living, sleeping or for the cooking and preparation of food. In most homes a passageway or landing provides this intervening ventilated space though in some instances a separate lobby has to be provided.

These provisions relating to ventilation must still be observed in modern building design. Most authorities today would accept that these requirements are essential for aesthetic, rather than for health, reasons. Ground-floor w.c. outlets connect, by means of a branch underground drain, to the nearest drain inspection chamber. Outlets of upper floor w.c.s are joined to an external soil-pipe by means of a short branch. The soil-pipe is continued, open-ended, to above eaves level to provide the drain with means of ventilation.

Waste appliances—sinks, baths, showers, wash basins and bidets—could be situated in, or immediately adjacent to, habitable rooms. Two barriers are therefore provided by the 'two pipe' system against the possible ingress of drain air. There is the trap provided at the outlet of the appliance and, as a further precaution, the waste pipe from the appliance is required to discharge over an external, trapped yard gully. Only the gully outlet could be connected directly to the drain.

At one time indeed the byelaws of some local authorities went even further. Waste pipes from sinks, baths and basins were not permitted to discharge directly over a yard gully but into an open channel, at least 18in long, connected to the gully. The simpler the plumbing system the more satisfactory the two pipe system of drainage was, and is, likely to prove.

In the 1920s and 1930s the great majority of houses intended 'for the working classes' (a phrase in common use in Acts of Parliament and elsewhere between the wars!) had just two plumbing fittings—an external w.c. and a shallow stoneware kitchen sink. If a bathroom was provided it was likely to be on the ground floor adjacent to the kitchen. The w.c. outlet connected directly to the underground drain. The sink and bath wastes discharged over a yard gully outside the kitchen. There were no problems. Difficulties arose when upstairs bathrooms became commonplace. An upstairs w.c. could discharge into the external soil/vent pipe, but how should the bath and wash basin wastes be dealt with?

The usual solution, in the provinces, was to run a length of rain water down-pipe discharging over a yard gully up the external wall of the house to a point just below the floor of the upstairs bathroom. A rain water hopper head would be inserted into its open upper end and the bath and basin waste pipes would discharge over this hopper head.

This was never a satisfactory arrangement. Soapy water would dry and decompose on the internal surfaces of the hopper and down-pipe. Smells resulting from this process (and smells from the yard gully below) would be carried up the down-pipe to discharge within a few feet of bathroom and bedroom windows. Thus, the very drain smells that the two pipe system was designed to eliminate would find their way into the house. The risk to health may have been minimal but the nuisance from smell was undeniable.

Recognising the defects of the rain water hopper head, the drainage byelaws of some local authorities (notably those of the former London County Council) forbade their use. They required the main waste pipe to discharge over a gully but insisted that the upper end should be treated in exactly the same way as the soil/vent pipe—it had to be taken open-ended to above eaves level. Branch waste pipes were connected to it in the same way that branch soil pipes were joined to the main soil and vent pipe. This arrangement was acceptable for one and two storey buildings with basic plumbing fittings.

Its disadvantages for multi-storey blocks of flats and hotels are obvious.

Prior to World War II, what was known as the 'one pipe' system of above-ground drainage was becoming commonly adopted for buildings of this kind. With the 'one-pipe' system —as with the 'single stack' system that has superseded it—the distinction between soil and waste appliances is abolished and all branch soil and waste pipes discharge into a single main soil and waste pipe. The danger that attends any installation in which a number of appliances drain into a single pipe is that of loss of seal from the trap beneath the appliance.

All sanitary fittings are provided with a trap at their outlet which retains sufficient water to prevent smells from the waste pipe or drain (the Victorians' 'drain air') from escaping. W.c.s and yard gullies have a built-in trap that forms an integral part of the appliance. A separate metal or plastic trap is fitted to the waste outlet of sinks, baths, basins and bidets (*Figure 7.2*).

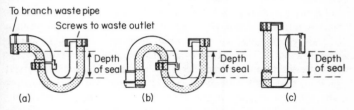

Fig. 7.2. Traps for sinks, basins, baths or bidets. (a) Tubular swivel trap with P outlet. (b) Tubular swivel trap with S outlet. (c) Bottle trap with P outlet

The simplest kind of trap is a U bend, usually made of copper, brass or lead, having an access eye with a screw-in cap fitted into its base. More attractive in appearance is the bottle trap, the whole of the lower part of which can be unscrewed for cleaning or clearance. Traps are described as 'P' traps if they have a more-or-less horizontal outlet and as 'S' traps if they have a vertical outlet. The 'seal' of the trap, that prevents the passage of drain air, is the vertical distance between the outlet of the trap and the upper part of the bend. With the two-pipe system it was usual for traps to have a 1½ in (37 mm) or 2in (50mm) seal. In order to ensure that drain smells cannot pass the trap it is essential that this seal should be maintained at all times.

Loss of seal may occur from momentum—a bucket of water thrown quickly and accurately down a w.c. may go straight through the trap leaving the seal broken—by evaporation, by 'waving out', by self-siphonage, by induced siphonage or by compression. Momentum and evaporation rarely present serious problems. Waving out is also a relatively rare phenomenon though it may be observed at times when a gusty wind is blowing across the top of a soil and vent pipe. The aspirating effect of the wind reduces pressure in the soil pipe and the water level in any w.c. attached to it can be seen to rise and fall with the gusts of wind. This movement creates its own momentum which, in time, can break the seal of the trap.

The connection of a number of appliances to a single drainage stack substantially increases the risks of self and induced siphonage and compression—and the unpleasantness that can result from these phenomena. *Some* self-siphonage occurs when any sanitary appliance is discharged. Water overflowing from the trap of a bath, sink or basin completely fills the waste pipe, taking air with it and producing the partial vacuum that induces siphonic action. This is not too important where baths and sinks are concerned. They have a relatively wide diameter—37mm (1½in)—waste pipe. After the siphon has been broken by air passing under the trap sufficient water will flow from the appliance to remake the seal. Basins are another matter. They have a small diameter—31mm (1¼in)—waste pipe that quickly fills with water as the basin discharges. There is relatively little subsequent drainage of water to recharge the trap.

With a two pipe drainage system temporary loss of seal from the trap of a waste appliance will not have serious consequences. The second line of defence, the seal of the yard gully, will remain intact. Only air from a relatively short length of waste pipe will be able to enter the room. With a one pipe or single stack system the situation is very different. Loss of seal can mean that smells from the main soil pipe, the underground drain and, in all probability, the sewer, can pass into the house.

'Induced siphonage' means siphonage of the water in the trap of one appliance resulting from the discharge of another appliance. Supposing, for instance, that a short length of branch waste pipe from a wash basin is connected to a waste pipe from a bath. The bath waste pipe will fill as the bath empties and water, flowing past the junction between the two waste pipes, will aspirate air from the basin branch. This will produce a partial vacuum within the branch and atmospheric pressure will push the water our of the basin's trap, breaking the seal.

'Compression' can result in a temporary loss of seal. It can also produce some extremely disconcerting results! Suppose that a combined soil and waste pipe connects to the underground drain with a sharp 'knuckle' bend. The discharge of a bath or w.c. may completely fill the pipe at the base of the bend, if only for a few moments. The discharge of another upstairs w.c. at that time will compress the air in the soil pipe

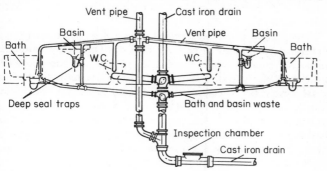

Fig. 7.3. One-pipe drainage system in cast iron

between the point of discharge and the point at which the soil pipe is temporarily obstructed. Air pressure within the pipe can then blow out the water seal of the trap of any appliance —perhaps a sink or a ground floor w.c.—connected to the soil pipe at low level.

Self-siphonage, induced siphonage and compression are prevented from occurring in a properly designed one-pipe system by ventilating the trap of each appliance (*Figure 7.3*). A small diameter vent pipe is taken from a point immediately behind each trap. This is connected to a main vent pipe which may be carried up to terminate open-ended above eaves level or, alternatively, connected to the main soil and vent pipe at a point at least 1m (3ft) above the highest soil or waste connection. Other precautions normally insisted upon in one-pipe drainage were deep seal (75mm or 3in) traps and an easy bend connection between the soil pipe and the underground drain.

A typical one-pipe system installed prior to about 1960 would have been constructed in heavy iron pipe, suitably protected against corrosion, with caulked lead joints. The main soil and waste stack and the main vent pipe would normally have been against an exterior wall though there was a tendency, particularly in good class hotel construction, to situate these pipes in service ducts within the structure of the building. A first class early example of this kind of installation is to be found at the Cumberland Hotel, Marble Arch, London.

The 'single stack' system of above ground drainage is a natural development of the one pipe system. First introduced into this country from the U.S.A. in the years immediately following World War II it was used experimentally, and somewhat hesitantly, for some multi-storey building construction during the 1950s. Two factors that have led to its almost universal adoption for all above-ground drainage work are the development of plastic soil and waste systems and the requirement of the Building Regulations that all soil and waste pipes must be contained within the fabric of the building.

This regulation has led to a revolutionary change in the external appearance of British buildings. Virtually any building constructed before the 1960s will be seen to have its walls festooned with soil and waste (or soil and vent) pipes. The back walls of suburban domestic properties have the down-pipe and hopper head arrangement of the two pipe system (*Figure 7.4a*). In contrast, the only visible evidence of drainage that can be seen on a building erected since the advent of the Building Regulations will be the rainwater guttering and downpipes and a short length of capped plastic vent pipe protruding a few inches above the surface of the roof (*Figure 7.4b*).

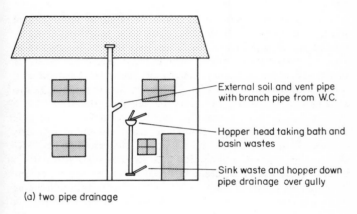

External soil and vent pipe with branch pipe from W.C.

Hopper head taking bath and basin wastes

Sink waste and hopper down pipe drainage over gully

(a) two pipe drainage

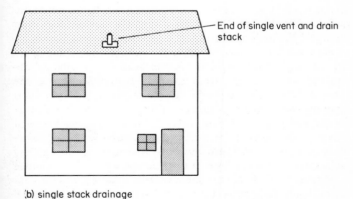

End of single vent and drain stack

(b) single stack drainage

Fig. 7.4. Two-pipe and single stack drainage compared

The essential difference between one-pipe and single-stack drainage is the elimination of trap ventilation. It has been found that, provided proper attention is given to design, the risk of siphonage and compression can be eliminated without the need for an extensive, and expensive, complex of ventilating pipes.

For really successful single stack installation the building should virtually be designed round the plumbing system. Branch waste pipes should be short and laid at minimal falls. This is particularly critical where the wash basin waste is concerned. The maximum length of the wash basin branch waste pipe should be 1.68m. Where a longer branch is unavoidable it is usually necessary to ventilate the trap of the wash basin as with a one-pipe system. A small vent pipe is connected immediately behind the trap and taken upwards to connect to the main soil and waste stack at least 1m (3ft) above the highest connection to it. Possible alternatives might be the use of a patent self-sealing trap or the expedient of taking the outlet of the trap into a 40mm or 50mm diameter waste pipe instead of the 30mm pipe usual for basin wastes.

Deep seal (75mm or 3in) traps should be used for all fittings. The w.c. branch connection should be 'swept' in the direction of flow and there should be an easy bend (minimum radius 200mm for 100mm stack pipes) between the main stack and the underground drain.

Measures must also be taken to ensure that there is no risk of bath, basin or bidet outlets becoming fouled or obstructed by discharges from the w.c. No connection to the main stack should be made for a distance of 200mm (8in) from the centre of the point at which the w.c. branch connects to the main stack (*Figure 7.5a*). This can pose a problem where bath, shower or bidet wastes are concerned. One solution is to offset these wastes so that they connect to the main stack below the level of the floor on which the appliance is situated. This is always inconvenient and can make a considerable addition to the cost of installation. It can be overcome by the use of the Marley collar boss. This fitting permits bath or bidet wastes to be discharged into an annular cavity between the collar and the connection taking the w.c. branch (*Figure 7.5b*).

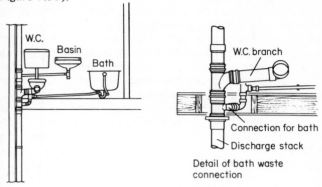

(a) Without Marley collar boss

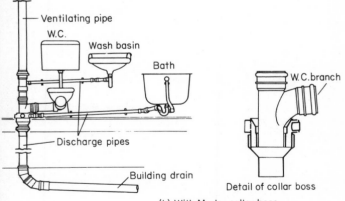

(b) With Marley collar boss

Fig. 7.5. Single stack drainage

Although single stack drainage is now commonly used for all waste drainage from all kinds of building it has few, if any, advantages over two pipe drainage for single storey (bungalow) development. Many designers prefer to limit the use of the single stack to upper floors in two or multistorey buildings.

Ground floor sinks, baths and basins can still discharge by means of short waste pipes over yard gullies. A very sensible provision of the Building Regulations requires that such waste pipes shall discharge above the level of the water in the gully but *below* the grid. This means that yards cannot flood with drainage water as a result of grids becoming blocked with leaves and other debris and also ensures that the full force of the waste pipe discharge is available to cleanse the gully.

Back and side inlet gullies are available to permit easy compliance with this requirement. Alternatively gully grids are available with slots in them through which the waste pipes can be passed.

8 Roof Drainage

Rainwater drainage from roofs is an important aspect of domestic plumbing for the design of which, in the past, rule of thumb methods have always been applied. On the whole rule of thumb methods have proved to be satisfactory.

'A little learning' might suggest that, since rainfall varies tremendously throughout the United Kingdom, gutter sizes and the number of downpipes provided should vary correspondingly. The roof of a house built in the Lake District, for instance, may be expected to receive, during the course of a year, three to four times as much rain as a house built in north-east Essex.

Design of roof drainage does not however depend upon total annual rainfall but upon rainfall intensity—and this varies very little from one part of the country to another. The average intensity recommended as a basis for rain water drainage design is 3in per hour. This has been found to occur, in any given locality, over a period of five minutes about every other year. It will occur over a period of ten minutes only about once in eight years. As an indication of the safety factor that is provided by designing on this basis it may be mentioned that an intensity of rainfall of 4in lasting for five minutes occurs only once in five years, for ten minutes only once in about nineteen years. For roof pitches up to 50° the actual area of the roof surface is taken as a basis for calculation. The pitch and the angle at which the rain falls is ignored. At 3in per hour the flow load will be 0.026 × actual roof area in square feet, giving a result in gallons per hour.

Prior to World War I rainwater gutters were almost invariably made of cast iron, painted internally and externally,

in either half-round, square or ogee pattern. Downpipes were
made of the same material. For a brief period during the
post-war years asbestos cement gutters and downpipes enjoyed
a certain popularity because, since they needed no painting,
they materially cut the cost of house maintenance. They
were however rather heavy, clumsy in appearance and subject
to accidental damage.

P.V.C. (vinyl) guttering and downspouts are now in standard
use for both new and replacement work. The smooth internal
surface of p.v.c. gives a better flow. No painting is required
either for decoration or for protection against corrosion and
the lightness in weight of the material makes for easy installation without the risk of damage to the material or injury to
the installer.

The *only* disadvantage of rainwater systems of this material
is that p.v.c. guttering does not offer adequate support for a
ladder. When access to the roof is required the ladder must be
placed against either the fascia board or the wall below it.
Although p.v.c. guttering is available in a number of sizes and
shapes 100mm (4in) wide, half-round gutter has become the
standard choice for general domestic use.

On the basis of the design considerations already set out a
gutter of this size, set dead level, will drain a roof having an
area of approximately 425 sq. ft. Where the gutter is laid to a
fall of 1in in 50ft (note that this is a fall of 1 in 600—not
1 in 50!) the area that can be drained is increased to 600 sq. ft.
68mm (about 2¾in) downpipe is used with 100mm guttering
and a downpipe of this size, centrally situated, will cope with
the drainage of a roof area of 1200 sq. ft. For all practical
purposes this means that 100mm half round guttering draining
into one 68mm downpipe will cope with the drainage of the
front roofs of a pair of terraced or semi-detached houses and
that similar provision will be needed at the back. 100mm
guttering with 68mm downpipes at front and back will cope
with the roof drainage of all but very large detached houses.

As has been suggested, rainwater guttering can be fixed
dead level. However the slight fall of 1in in 50ft improves
drainage capacity and guards against the possibility of a

slight accidental back-fall—perhaps the commonest cause of overflowing gutters.

All manufacturers of plastic waste and soil drainage systems include roof drainage systems within their range and supply full installation instructions. The details given below relate to the Marley system of 100mm half-round guttering with 68mm down-pipes. The first thing that must be established is the position of the gutter outlet. In a new building this will be decided by design considerations bearing in mind the effect of appearance of the downpipe on the facade of the building. For replacement work the deciding factor will be the position of the existing yard gully. A plumb-line dropped from the fascia board to the centre of this gully will establish the position of the gutter outlet.

Working back from this point with a line at a fall of 1in in 50ft the position of the supporting brackets can be determined (*Figure 8.1*). Brackets must be fitted in close proximity

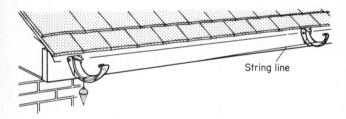

Fig. 8.1. Aligning the gutter brackets

to and on either side of the gutter outlet. They must also be fitted closely to both internal and external angles of the roof (*Figure 8.2*). For straight runs of guttering, brackets should be fitted at 1 metre centres with Marley heavy gauge guttering and at no greater than 900mm centres for the lighter 'System 2' guttering. Brackets should be fixed to the fascia board with 1in X No.8 gauge zinc plated or sherardised round head screws.

Marley 'heavy grade' roof guttering is provided with one socketed end and one notched spigot end. 'System 2' guttering

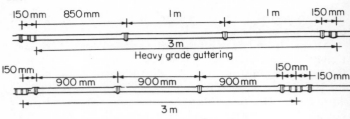

System 2 guttering on straight runs

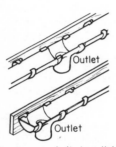

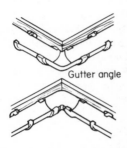

In close proximity to outlets

In close proximity to external and internal angles

Fig. 8.2. Position of gutter brackets

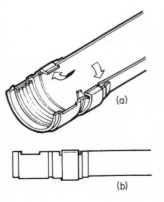

Fig. 8.3. Assembling a Marley gutter joint. To assemble a joint, clip the gutter strap round the gutter socket or the fitting socket between the notches. Turn the end of the gutter into the socket so that the back edge of the strap fits into the notch (a). Press down the front edge of the gutter until it snaps under the front of the strap. This compresses the rubber seal to form a watertight joint. Finally, line up the notches so that the strap is in the centre of the notches (b)

has notched spigot ends only and separate Marley gutter joints must be used for connecting lengths of gutter. In both cases however the method of connection is the same.

The flexible plastic gutter strap is clipped round the socket of the gutter or of the separate gutter joint. The spigot of the other length of gutter is then placed in the socket and turned so that the retaining projection of the back edge of the gutter strap fits into the notch of the spigot (*Figure 8.3*). The front edge of the spigot is then eased down into the socket until its notch snaps under the front projection of the gutter strap. This has the effect of compressing the spigot against the prefixed synthetic rubber seal to give a watertight joint.

It will be seen that the notch in the spigot of the gutter is an essential feature of the patent Marley joint. Where it is necessary to cut a length of gutter a similar notch must be made in the cut end. The gutter should be cut absolutely squarely with a fine toothed saw and a notch 40mm wide and 3mm deep made 10mm from the end (*Figure 8.4*). A special notching tool is made for this purpose but it is possible to make the necessary notch with a file.

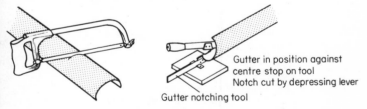

Gutter in position against
centre stop on tool
Notch cut by depressing lever

Gutter notching tool

Fig. 8.4. Cutting and notching a length of gutter. The gutter must be cut perfectly squarely with a fine toothed saw (a). The notch is then cut 40 mm wide, 3 mm deep, 10 mm from the end using a fine toothed saw and a file. A special notching tool can also be used (b)

The first task to be undertaken in connection with the fixing of the downpipe is assembly of the offset. Marley offsets have three components—an offset end socket for connection to the gutter outlet, an offset end for connection to the downpipe and a length of offcut rain water pipe to connect the two (*Figure 8.5*). The offset is made into one unit by means of solvent welding. This technique, which is used for connecting p.v.c. water supply and waste pipes, is described fully in Chapter 12. The instructions set out below relate solely to rain water offsets.

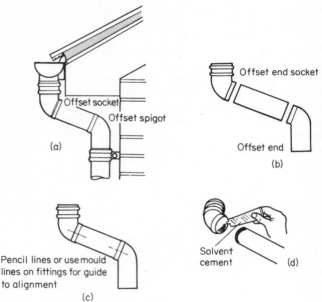

Fig. 8.5. Assembling the offset using solvent welds. The offset (a) can be made up using an offset socket, an offset spigot and an offcut of pipe (b) as follows. (1) Cut the pipe to length and remove all rough edges. (2) Using a dry cloth, clean the outside of pipe ends and the internal surfaces of sockets. (3) Assemble the offset and draw pencil lines to ensure correct alignment (c). (4) Apply a thin layer of solvent cement to the ends of the pipe and inside the sockets (d) and fit sockets and pipe together, ensuring that the pencil marks line up

The offcut length of rain water downpipe must be cut squarely to length and all rough edges removed. Wipe internal surfaces of the solvent weld sockets and the outside of the pipe end perfectly clean with a dry cloth. Next assemble the offset dry and draw a pencil line along pipe and offset ends to ensure correct alignment. Withdraw pipe from offset ends and apply solvent cement evenly round the spigot ends of the offcut and the inside of the offset sockets. Press pipe and offset sockets quickly and firmly together taking care to line up with the pencil guide lines that have already been made. Leave the completed offset for several minutes before fitting into position to ensure that the joints set properly.

Various offset components are available to overcome the problems that may arise from, for instance, a deep fascia or a corbel projection. Rainwater downpipe components are provided with ring seal sockets but the ring seal is not normally inserted in external rainwater work. Since the downpipe should

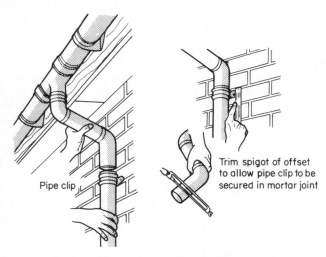

Pipe clip

Trim spigot of offset to allow pipe clip to be secured in mortar joint

Fig. 8.6. Aligning the pipe clip with a mortar joint

never run full a ring seal is normally unnecessary and the absence of such a seal makes it possible to locate quickly any blockage that may occur.

However, where an eaves projects more than 600mm there will be a tendency for the weight of the offset to pull the offset away from the gutter outlet. To counteract this tendency a ring seal should be provided for large eaves projections.

The offset spigot for connection to the rainwater downpipe is 112mm long. This allows for adjustment of the position of the first pipe clip. Offer up the socket of the first downpipe to the spigot of the offset. If the holes of the pipe bracket back plate do not align with a mortar joint, measure the amount of spigot that needs to be cut off in order that the pipe clip can be fixed to the next joint up (*Figure 8.6*).

Two kinds of pipe clip are available. A one-piece clip and a two piece unit in which the plastic strap that supports the pipe socket is bolted to a back plate secured to the wall. In both cases the mortar joint should be drilled and plugged with purpose made fibre or plastic plugs and the back plate—or the clip itself in the case of the one-piece unit—secured to the wall with two 1½in or 1¼in by No.10g zinc plated or sherardised round head steel screws. A clip should be located at the socket of each length of rainwater downpipe and an intermediate clip provided for any length of downpipe exceeding 2 metres. An important point to note is that an expansion gap of 10mm should be left between the end of each pipe and the bottom of the socket into which it is fitted. This is done by inserting the pipe to its fullest extent into the socket, withdrawing 10mm and marking the point to which it has been withdrawn.

Various means of connecting the rainwater downpipe to an underground drainage system are illustrated in *Figure 8.7*. A trapped gully should always be used where the rainwater is disposed of into a sewerage system. Where discharge is into a soakaway or ditch an untrapped connection is permissible.

Ultimate disposal of the rainwater will depend upon the policy of the sewerage authority. In some areas some, or all, rainwater from roofs is permitted to flow into the normal household drainage system and thence to the public sewer. This results in the sewerage authority having to provide unnecessarily large sewers to cope with the surge that occurs at times of intense rainfall. It means too that the sewage arriving at the treatment works will be highly concentrated in times of drought and very dilute during periods of heavy rainfall.

These factors have led many authorities to require separate provision for rainwater drainage. In some areas a separate

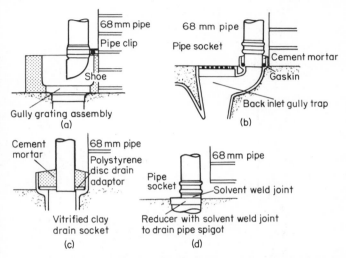

Fig. 8.7. Connecting the rainwater downpipe to the underground drain. (a) With a shoe above the grating of a trapped gully. (b) Joined to the back or side inlet of a gully trap. (c) or (d) Connected direct to the drain with an adaptor

surface water sewer is provided. In these areas it is *very important* that the builder should make the ultimate connection, of both the foul and the surface water drain, to the right sewer. Connection of the foul drain to the surface water sewer can result in untreated sewage flowing into a stream or ditch. In other areas the householder is required to provide a soakaway for the reception of rainwater drainage from roofs.

Typically a soakaway consists of a rectangular pit about 5ft deep and 5ft square in plan. This is filled with brick rubble to within about 1ft of the surface and the top soil is then replaced. The snag about a soakaway of this kind is that, after a few

years, the interstices between the rubble will become full of
silt and the soakaway will then have to be dug out and remade.
This eventuality can be delayed by laying a sheet of polythene
over the brick rubble before back-filling with top soil.

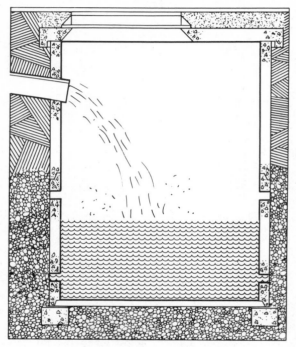

*Fig. 8.8. Precast concrete soakaway. Where it is not possible
to dispose of surface water by a drainage pipe system it can
be done by a system of soakaways, provided that the soil is
permeable*

There are nowadays precast concrete soakaways available
into which rainwater can be discharged (*Figure 8.8*). These
resemble cesspools but have holes in the sides from which
water can escape into the surrounding soil. A manhole gives
access to enable the silt to be dug out when required.

It should perhaps be added that soakaways are rarely very successful except where the soil is light and friable and there is a low subsoil 'water table'. Few soakaways will cope adequately with long periods of continuous, heavy rain.

9 The Underground Drains

The basic principles involved in the design of underground drainage systems have remained virtually unchanged for over half a century. Underground drains must be laid in straight lines, to a constant self-cleansing fall. They must be watertight and must remain watertight even if there should be slight soil settlement. Every point of the drainage system must be accessible for rodding in the event of a blockage occurring.

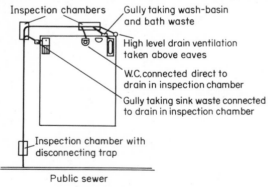

Fig. 9.1. Plan of traditional house drainage

Branch connections must join the main drain obliquely in the direction of flow. The drainage system must be adequately ventilated (*Figure 9.1*). The development of new materials has however resulted in revolutionary changes taking place in the way in which these principles are observed.

Up to about 1950, only two materials were used for underground drainage work—either salt glazed stoneware pipes or heavy iron pipes suitably protected against corrosion. Glazed stoneware pipes were commonly used for domestic drains. They were 4in in internal diameter and 2ft in length, and were usually laid upon a 6in thick 'raft' of concrete to give them some stability in the event of ground settlement (*Figure 9.2*).

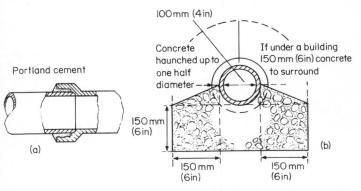

Fig. 9.2. Jointing of stoneware drain pipe (a) and base of a stoneware drain (b)

The multitudinous joints—each a potential point of leakage—were made by caulking a tarred rope grommet into the space between spigot and drain socket and completing the joint with either neat portland cement or a mixture of two parts cement to one of sand. The purpose of the rope grommet was to prevent the jointing material entering the drain to impede free flow and establishing a cause of blockage.

To be absolutely certain that no jointing material had leaked through it was usual to draw a sack through the completed drain by a length of rope. The inspector of the local authority would, before passing the drain for use, check on this point by observation with the aid of a mirror and an electric torch and, perhaps, by rolling a ball through the drain. After the drain was laid it was usual to haunch it over with concrete to increase its strength. Where a stoneware drain

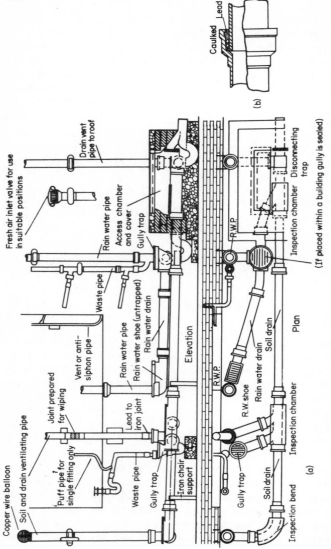

Fig. 9.3. Layout of iron drainage system (a) and jointing of iron pipes (b)

passed under a building it was covered entirely by a layer of concrete 6in thick.

Iron drainpipes were considerably more expensive and were used in good class industrial and commercial work (*Figure 9.3*). They were obtainable in 9ft lengths, thus reducing the number of joints. These were made by caulking lead wool into the space between spigot and socket. Iron drains were not required to be laid on a concrete base.

It has been established empirically that drains are self-cleansing when water flows through them at 3ft per second when one third full. A universally adopted rule of thumb allowed for a fall of 1 in 40 (3in in 10ft) for the usual 4in drain and a fall of 1 in 60 for the 6in drains that might be used where a number of houses were drained in combination.

Even with the many-jointed stoneware drains this gave a flow in excess of 3ft per second if the drain were laid to a steady fall and it should perhaps be stressed that too steep a fall is almost as undesirable as a too shallow one. If the fall of the drain is too steep there is a tendency for liquid to flow on in advance of solid matter that may be left behind to form a blockage. However, for most purposes, the 1 in 40 rule worked well enough.

Access to every part of the drain was ensured by the provision of inspection chambers or 'manholes' at every change of direction of the main drain and at every point where a branch drain connected to it. Inspection chambers were constructed of brickwork on a 6in concrete base and it was usual to render the internal surfaces of the inspection chamber walls with a sand and cement mixture. The drain flowed through the inspection chamber in a half-channel built into the base and concrete was haunched up on either side of the half-channel and trowelled to a smooth sand and cement surface. Purpose made 'three quarter bends' could be built into the haunching to permit branches to connect in the direction of flow.

Access to the inspection chamber was obtained by raising a cast iron manhole cover set into a frame of the same material. On the rare occasions that it was necessary to construct an inspection chamber within a building the cover would be 'double sealed' and set into the frame in a bed of grease to prevent gases from the drain escaping.

The inspection chambers of iron drains did not need to be made watertight as special access sections were manufactured with bolted down iron covers. The bolts could be unscrewed and the cover removed when access was required to the drain.

In the final inspection chamber before the connection of the drain to the sewer (usually situated near the front boundary of the property) it was common practice to provide an intercepting or disconnecting trap (*Figure 9.4*). The purpose of this trap was to prevent gases, and perhaps rats, from the sewer from entering the house drains.

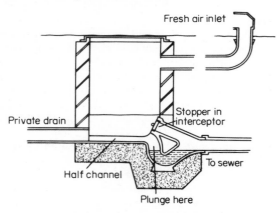

Fig. 9.4. Inspection chamber with intercepting trap and fresh air inlet

The value of the intercepting trap was questioned as early as 1912 by the Departmental Committee on Intercepting Traps and House Drains. A well constructed and maintained sewer should contain neither rats nor offensive gases. If the intercepting trap were omitted the sewer would be ventilated very thoroughly by means of the soil and vent pipe of each individual drainage system. There would be no need for separate sewer ventilators. Furthermore, the intercepting trap was and—where it is installed—still is, the commonest site of drain blockage. The trap inevitably impedes the flow of water and tends to permit solid matter to accumulate in its base. To make intercepting traps rather less liable to blockage they were constructed with a sharp weir inlet and an easy outlet 2in lower than the inlet. For this design to have the desired effect of making the trap more or less self-cleansing it was, of course, essential that it should be set dead level.

Intercepting traps are provided with a rodding arm to permit the clearance of that section of the drain that lies between the trap and the sewer. The rodding arm has a socket inlet closed with a stoneware stopper. This stopper is a common cause of a particularly unpleasant form of partial drain stoppage that can sometimes remain undetected for months.

Any increase of pressure within the sewer—arising from, for instance, a surge of storm water—is liable to push the stopper out of its socket. It will fall into the inlet to the intercepting trap immediately beneath it and will promptly cause a blockage. The blockage will not however be discovered in the usual way because sewage will rise in the inspection chamber until it reaches the level of the, now open, rodding arm and will be able to flow down this arm to the sewer. The liquid in the bottom of the inspection chamber will, in the meantime, become steadily more and more foul until the defect makes itself obvious by the unpleasant smell that greets visitors near the front gate of the property. Complaints of 'drain smells' in front gardens are nearly always attributable to this cause.

Where this trouble has arisen it is usually better *not* to replace the stopper in the socket of the rodding arm. Cut a disc of slate or glass to size and cement it lightly into this socket. On the rare occasions that it may be necessary to rod through to the sewer the glass or slate can be broken with a crow bar and can then be replaced after the blockage has been cleared.

If a drain has an intercepting trap it will usually also be provided with a low level drain ventilator connected to the same inspection chamber. This consists of a length of drain-pipe connected to the inspection chamber and protruding a few inches above ground level. Into the open end is inserted a metal box with a grille at the front. A hinged mica flap is suspended inside the ventilator against this grille. In theory air passing over the top of the open soil and vent pipe would aspirate air out of the drain. The reduction in pressure would result in the outside air pushing open the hinged flap and flowing into and through the drain from low level. In the event of a back pressure within the drain the mica flap would press tightly against the grille and drain air would not escape.

Unfortunately low level ventilators are particularly susceptible to accidental damage and to vandalism. Before long the grille becomes damaged and the mica flap either damaged or jammed in position. A glance into the front gardens of any suburban street developed during the 1920s or 1930s will confirm this. It will, in fact, be found that many householders have removed and sealed off the low level ventilator or 'fresh air inlet' as serving no useful purpose and being a recurring source of unpleasant smells. If the intercepting trap is omitted there is, of course, no need whatsoever for a fresh air inlet.

Modern underground drains are likely to be of p.v.c. or pitch fibre with push-on ring seal joints. Both the drains and the means by which they are joined are sufficiently flexible to absorb slight ground settlement without damage. A concrete base is therefore unnecessary. Proper preparation of the bed on which the drains are to be laid remains important however. Where the subsoil consists of heavy clay or chalk it may be necessary to prepare an imported bed of gravel to form a base. Infilling of the drain trenches must also be undertaken with some care to avoid the risk of accidental damage. Drain gradients may be considerably less than was considered necessary with many-jointed stoneware drains. Falls of 1 in 60 or 1 in 70 are in common use.

Inspection chambers are no less necessary than they were in the past and they may still be built of brickwork in the traditional manner (*Figure 9.5*). They should not however be rendered *internally* with sand and cement to make them watertight. Experience has shown that internal rendering is liable to crack and flake off the walls, causing drain blockages.

131

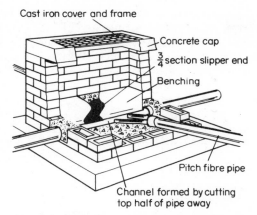

Cast iron cover and frame
Concrete cap
$\frac{3}{4}$ section slipper end
Benching
Pitch fibre pipe
Channel formed by cutting
top half of pipe away

Fig. 9.5. Pitch fibre drain taken through brick built inspection chamber

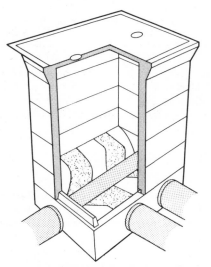

Fig. 9.6. Pitch fibre drain pipes taken through sectional concrete inspection chamber

If an inspection chamber is to be rendered it should be to the external walls, before the soil is filled in round the chamber.

Complete prefabricated inspection chambers made of fibre-glass reinforced plastic are now available and can speed up installation work. Alternatively inspection chambers can

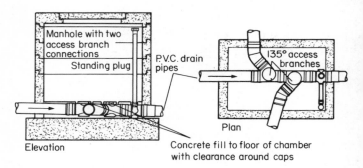

Fig. 9.7. Marley sealed access drainage system. As the drains are sealed inspection chambers need not be watertight. The standing plug allows any ground water to be drained away into the drain

be constructed on the site from precast concrete sections (*Figure 9.6*). Marley Extrusions have now produced a sealed access p.v.c. drainage system resembling in many respects the sealed iron systems referred to earlier in this chapter (*Figure 9.7*).

Blocked drains

Blockages may occur in any part of the drainage system, either above or below ground. Above-ground blockages are most likely to occur in the traps of baths, basins or sinks. The waste stopper is removed and the fitting fails to empty. The immediate course of action should be to try plunging with a sink plunger or 'force cup' (*Figure 9.8*). In the great majority of cases this will produce a speedy remedy.

A force cup is a hemisphere of rubber or plastic usually mounted on the end of a wooden handle. Hold a damp cloth firmly over the overflow outlet of the fitting. Place the force cup over the waste outlet and plunge down forcibly three or four times. Since water cannot be compressed the force of this action is transmitted to the obstruction to move it. The purpose of the damp cloth held over the overflow outlet is to prevent the dissipation of this force.

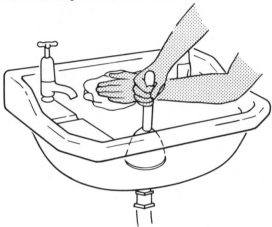

Fig. 9.8. Clearing a blockage in a basin, bath or sink waste with a force cap or sink waste plunger

If plunging fails to clear the blockage gain access to the trap. The traditional U bend trap has an access eye at or near its base from which the stopper can be unscrewed. The entire base of a bottle trap can be unscrewed and removed. Before attempting this place an empty bucket under the trap. Probing with a piece of wire after having gained access to the trap will usually dislodge the cause of the blockage.

A poor flow from a sink, bath or wash basin when the stopper has been removed suggests the presence of a partial blockage. This could be due to hair or other debris clinging to the waste grid. In this case the remedy is obvious. A build-up of grease on the interior surfaces of the waste pipe is another possibility. One of the proprietary chemical drain cleaners can be used to clear this. These chemicals usually have a caustic soda base and should be handled with care.

There are two ways in which a blocked underground drain may come to the attention of the householder. A gully may flood or drainage be seen escaping from under the cover of an inspection chamber; or a w.c., when flushed, may fill almost to the brim with water which will then very slowly subside.

If a flooded gully is the first indication first raise the grid to make sure that the trouble is not due simply to leaves or other obstruction on the grid itself.

Having cleared this point raise the drain inspection covers to establish the position of the blockage. If, for instance, the chamber nearest to the house is flooded but the one near the boundary of the property is clear, then the obstruction must be in the length of drain between these two inspection chambers.

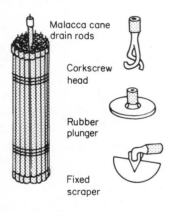

Malacca cane
drain rods

Corkscrew
head

Rubber
plunger

Fixed
scraper

Fig. 9.9. A set of drain rods with useful alternative heads

A set of drain rods, or sweeps rods, are necessary to effect a clearance (*Figure 9.9*). Screw two or three drain rods together, plunge one end into the flooded inspection chamber and feel for the half-channel at its base. Push the end of the rod along this half-channel and into the underground drain in the direction of the blockage. Screw on more lengths of drain rod as necessary and continue to thrust into the drain until the obstruction is encountered and cleared.

A variety of tools are available that can be screwed onto the end of drain rods to clear difficult obstructions. Twisting the rods will make it easier to push them into the drain and to withdraw them afterwards. Be sure to twist clockwise only. Twisting in the other direction will result in the rods becoming unscrewed and lost in the drain.

If all inspection chambers are flooded and the drain has an intercepting trap, the probability is that it is in this trap that the obstruction is situated. It can be dealt with by plunging. Screw two or three drain rods together and screw a 4in drain plunger onto the end. This is a 4in diameter rubber disc with a screwed socket for connection to drain rods.

Lower the plunger into the inspection chamber containing the intercepting trap. Feel for the half-channel at its base and move along this channel until the drop into the trap is encountered. Plunge down sharply two or three times. The chances are that there will be a gurgle as the obstruction is cleared and water level in the inspection chambers will fall quickly as water flows through freely into the sewer.

In an emergency an old fashioned household mop on a long handle—or even a bundle of rags *securely* tied to a broom stick—can be pressed into service as a drain plunger.

After clearing a drain the sides and benching of the inspection chambers should be washed down with hot soda and taps should be left running for half an hour or so to flush out the drain and half channels.

Some legal considerations

House owners should be aware of the fact that their responsibility for their house drains does not end at the boundary of the property. It extends to the public sewer usually situated in the highway.

Blockages and other defects in the length of drain between the property boundary and the sewer are fortunately rare. Remedying them can be very expensive especially when it is necessary to excavate to expose the defective drain. Builders should therefore exercise extreme care in laying this length of drain, in making the actual connection to the sewer and in back-filling.

Other, somewhat complex, considerations arise where (as is very frequently the case) a number of houses are drained in combination (*Figure 9.10*). This obviously saves initial costs.

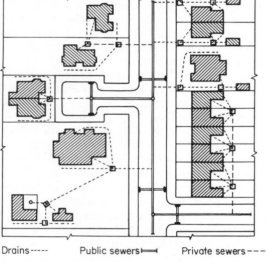

Drains----- Public sewers⊢══◀ Private sewers---

Fig. 9.10. Houses drained in combination—drains, private sewers and public sewers. The lengths marked as 'private sewers' in the plan would in fact be 'public sewers' if constructed before 1 October 1937

There is only one deep excavation to the sewer, only one sewer connection and only one reinstatement of the road surface. The difficulty arises when a section of 'combined drain' becomes blocked or otherwise defective and responsibility for remedying the defect has to be determined.

The legal position is that combined drains of this kind, constructed before the coming into effect of the Public Health Act 1936 on 1 October 1937, are 'public sewers'—

but they are public sewers with a difference. The sewerage authority is responsible for any repairs, maintenance or 'cleansing' that may be necessary but can recover the cost of maintenance and repair (but not of 'cleansing') from the owners of the properties concerned. 'Cleansing' is generally taken to include the clearance of blockages and, except in the case of a recurring blockage due to a defect in the 'public sewer' this will usually be undertaken free of charge. Drains serving more than one property that were constructed subsequent to 1 October 1937 are 'private sewers' and are wholly the responsibility of the owners of the properties concerned.

Details of the connection to the private sewer and the responsibility that this entails should be (but rarely are) set out in the deeds of each individual house. It cannot be stressed too strongly that owners of properties connected to such a sewer should establish, with the other owners concerned, responsibility for repair, maintenance and clearance *before trouble actually occurs.*

It is not unusual for as many as ten or twelve properties on a new housing estate to be connected to a single private sewer. A blockage or other defect near to the public sewer may have no visible effect whatsoever on the drainage of properties at the head of this private sewer though their sewage may be flooding the gardens of houses at a lower level. It is far too late to attempt to explain the situation once this has occurred.

When in doubt consult the Environmental Health Officer of the local District or Borough Council. His advice may lack legal authority but is likely to be based on common sense and experience of a score of similar situations.

Rural drainage

Everything so far written in this chapter has assumed the existence of a public sewer to which the house drains will be connected. This is by no means necessarily the case. There are many rural areas where no public sewerage system exists and many isolated houses to which a public sewer can never

economically be taken. Such houses, if they are to have a
water carriage system of drainage, must be connected either to
a cesspool or a septic tank.

Details of the construction of a cesspool or septic tank
system are hardly appropriate to a *beginner's* guide to plumbing
but it is important that all householders and builders who may
be concerned with such installations should be aware of the
differences between a cesspool and a septic tank and should
be familiar with the principles involved.

A cesspool is simply a watertight underground chamber
intended for the reception and storage of sewage until such
time as it can be pumped out and disposed of. Cesspools may
be constructed of brickwork rendered watertight with sand
and cement (*Figure 9.11*), of precast concrete rings set into a
concrete base or of fibreglass reinforced plastic (*Figure 9.12*).

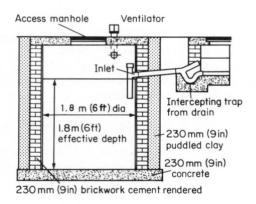

*Fig. 9.11. Typical cesspool serving pre-Building
Regulations cottage*

Capacity may be as little as 500 gallons or may be 4000 gallons
or more. The Building Regulations prescribe 4000 gallons as
the minimum capacity of a modern cesspool but, of course,
the great majority of existing cesspools were constructed long
before the Building Regulations came into effect.

Cesspool owners are constantly surprised at the speed with which their cesspools fill and require emptying. A little thought will establish that there is nothing very surprising about this.

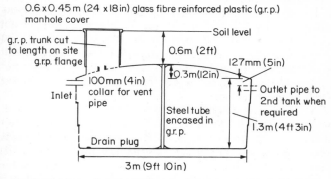

Fig. 9.12. 2000 gallon capacity plastic/glass fibre cesspool (Rokcrete Ltd, Clacton-on-Sea)

It has been estimated that water consumption for all domestic purposes—drinking, cooking and preparation of food, baths, laundry, w.c. flushing and so on—amounts to between 20 and 25 gal per person per day. Taking the lower of these two figures a family of two adults and two children might be expected to use at least 80 gallons of water a day. Every drop of this water passes into the drain, and thence into the cesspool, in one form or another. Such a family could therefore fill a 500 gal cesspool in less than a week and a 1000 gal cesspool (the usual size prior to the Building Regulations) in under a fortnight!

The fact that cesspools do not often require to be emptied *quite* as frequently as this is usually attributable to the fact that few cesspools are wholly watertight. This too however can be a mixed blessing. A cesspool that permits its contents to leak out will permit subsoil water to leak in. A leaky cesspool, in an area where subsoil water level is high, may, during prolonged wet weather, fill up again almost before the Council's cesspool emptier has returned to its depot.

The prospective purchaser of a property with cesspool drainage should check the capacity of the cesspool and the availability and cost of the local cesspool emptying service. The local authorities of districts in which unsewered properties are situated normally operate a cesspool emptying service. If they do not do so the Council's Environmental Health Department will certainly be able to suggest a local private contractor. These are matters that deserve very careful consideration. Cesspool emptying is, at the best, a smelly and unpleasant operation. It can also prove to be a very expensive one for the householder.

A septic tank system is quite unlike a cesspool in that it offers a permanent solution for the *disposal* of sewage—not merely for its storage. It is, in fact, a small private sewage treatment plant. Small septic tank systems may serve individual houses while larger ones can be used to cope with the sewage of isolated groups of houses. To understand the operation of a septic tank installation it is essential to know something about the chemical and bacteriological processes of decomposition.

In the public mind bacteria or 'germs' are generally thought of as being malign organisms responsible for the spread of disease. In fact the bacteria responsible for disease are the exceptions. The overwhelming majority of the myriads of bacteria with which the world teems are wholly benevolent to other forms of life. Neither vegetable nor animal life could continue without their activities. These activities consist of the breaking down, or decomposition, of dead organic matter into its basic chemical constituents. The action of bacteria breaks down organic matter, first into offensively smelling ammoniacal compounds and then into harmless nitrites and nitrates. The nitrates provide nourishment for plants, some of which become the food of animals—including ourselves. Animals, and of course dead and dying plants, produce dead organic matter which is again broken down into its chemical constituents by bacterial action. This cyclical action is described as the 'nitrogen cycle'. All life on this planet depends upon the continuation of this cycle in which bacteria play a vital role. The purpose of a septic tank installation is to ensure that the bacterial process of decomposition takes place rapidly and under controlled conditions.

The septic tank itself is an underground chamber designed to retain sewage for at least twenty four hours. Sewage enters and leaves by means of dip pipes extending well below the level of the liquid in the tank when full. The surface of the liquid therefore remains undisturbed. A baffle, or system of baffles, may also be provided within the tank to prevent the rapid flow of water from inlet to outlet when, for instance, a bath is discharged. Within the septic tank sewage is liquefied by the action of anaerobic bacteria—bacteria which cannot live in the presence of free oxygen. A scum forms on the surface of the liquid in the tank, retaining the unpleasant smells, and a sludge forms at the base. The sludge must be pumped out from time to time. Twice yearly desludging has been recommended but this is probably a counsel of perfection. It is not unusual for septic tanks to operate satisfactorily for several years without desludging.

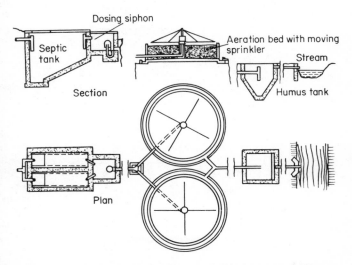

Fig. 9.13. Large septic tank installation suitable for groups of houses

Anaerobic action within the septic tank is only the first part of the bacteriological process of purification. The liquid effluent from the tank must next be submitted to thorough and systematic aeration to encourage aerobic bacteria (bacteria which thrive in the presence of free oxygen) to complete the process. This is usually done by permitting the effluent to percolate through a 'filter' bed of clinker or granite chippings. One cubic yard of filtering or aerating material is required for every forty gallons of estimated daily flow.

Arrangements must be made to ensure that the effluent is distributed evenly over the filter bed. Larger installations will be circular and the effluent will be distributed by means of revolving arms activated by the weight of the liquid leaving the septic tank (*Figure 9.13*). Simpler arrangements are

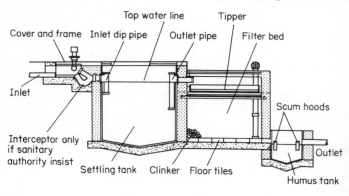

Fig. 9.14. Septic tank and filter system designed by Burn Bros. Ltd

permissible with smaller installations. A tipper device may be used to spill the effluent onto perforated corrugated asbestos sheets, first on one side of the filter and then on the other (*Figure 9.14*). The Gibson-Ingol annular septic tank and filter unit (*Figure 9.15*) has a septic tank, circular in plan, in which

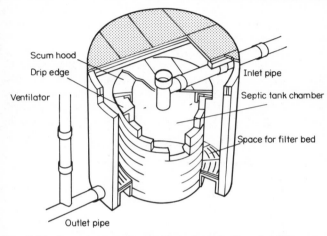

Fig. 9.15. Precast concrete septic tank and filter by Gibson-Ingol Ltd, Preston

the inlet to the tank is at its centre and the effluent spills over onto a circular filter bed provided round the outside wall of the tank. The effluent from the filter can usually be discharged directly into any convenient ditch or stream. With large installations however a further small settlement tank, with baffles, may be provided to trap the small particles of black 'humus' present in the final effluent.

Where there is a light and absorbent subsoil, no sources of water in the vicinity and a sufficient area of land, it may sometimes be possible to dispense with the filter section of the septic tank unit and to dispose of the effluent by subsoil irrigation. Land drains for this purpose should be laid flat, or almost flat, on a 1ft deep bed of clinker or brick-bats. There should be a further 1ft of this material on each side of the

pipe line and above it. To reduce the risk of the irrigation
system becoming clogged with grit washing down from the
soil above it is a good idea to cover the bed of clinker with a
polythene sheet before back-filling the trench.

Traditionally, land drain pipes are of earthenware and are
laid butt jointed. However perforated pitch fibre or p.v.c.
land drainage pipes are obtainable in long lengths and offer a
much more satisfactory modern alternative.

It is usual for the effluent from the septic tank to flow
directly into the pipes of the irrigation system. This tends to
result in the soil in the immediate vicinity of the tank becoming very heavily charged with sewage while little or no
effluent reaches the further end of the pipe line. The provision of a final dosing chamber with an automatic siphon

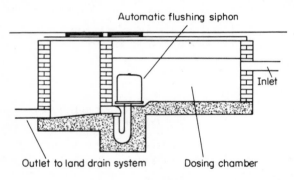

*Fig. 9.16. Automatic flushing siphon for effluent disposal
by subsoil irrigation*

will prevent this (*Figure 9.16*). The level of effluent will rise
in the dosing chamber until it reaches the inverted U bend of
the siphon. Siphonic action will then take place, emptying
the dosing chamber and distributing the effluent throughout
the land drainage system. This ensures even distribution of
the effluent, prevents the soil in the immediate vicinity of the
septic tank from being overloaded and soured and ensures a
period of time, after each flush, in which the soil bacteria can
act upon the discharged effluent. A properly designed septic

tank installation requires little or no maintenance beyond periodic removal of sludge from the septic tank.

Excessive use of disinfectants should be avoided within the home since these will destroy the bacteria upon which septic action depends as well as the germs of disease. For the same reason the salt wash from a mains water softener should not be permitted to flow into a septic tank. Brine has antiseptic qualities.

For a rather different reason the *excessive* use of household detergents should be avoided in a house drained to a septic tank. These tend to emulsify the fats present in sewage. Instead of a scum forming on the top of the septic tank and a sludge at the bottom, the tank will be filled with a liquid of soup-like consistency that will be washed through to clog the filter or land drainage system.

Rain water, whether from roofs or yard surfaces, should of course be rigidly excluded from any cesspool or septic tank drainage system.

10 Hard and Soft Water

Whether a water supply is 'hard' or 'soft' depends upon the nature of its journey from raincloud to the Water Authority's reservoir.

Water has the capacity to take into solution some part of practically any gas or solid matter with which it comes into contact. Even during its brief journey from the clouds to the earth it will take into solution measurable quantities of carbon dioxide and, where it falls over a town, sulphur dioxide and other pollutants of the atmosphere. If it falls onto mountains or moorland it will acquire acid characteristics as it flows, via streams and rivers, to the reservoir. Such water will be soft and will have a tendency towards plumbosolvency—the characteristic of dissolving lead from the surfaces of water pipes.

If, on the other hand, it falls on a chalky soil, or seeps through the various strata of the earth into natural underground storage reservoirs it will dissolve the bicarbonates, sulphates and chlorides of calcium and magnesium from the rock and soil surfaces with which it comes into contact. These are the chemicals that are responsible for hardness in water. Virtually all water supplies in southern England, the south Midlands and East Anglia are hard or very hard. Water supplies in Wales, Scotland and the north of England are predominantly soft though, even in these areas, pockets of hard water supply are to be found.

Hardness is usually expressed in terms of the equivalent of calcium carbonate in the water in parts per million though 'degrees of hardness' on Clark's scale are sometimes used. One degree of hardness on this scale is equal to 14 parts per million or p.p.m. Water containing the equivalent of more than 100 p.p.m. of calcium carbonate is reckoned to be 'moderately hard' and water containing over 200 p.p.m. is 'hard'. Some 65% of the homes in Great Britain are supplied with water that would be classified as hard or moderately hard.

The householder who writes to his Water Authority enquiring about the hardness of the local water supply will probably be given three figures; 'temporary hardness', 'permanent hardness' and the sum of the two, 'total hardness'.

'Temporary hardness' is hardness that can be removed by boiling and is the kind that is most serious from the point of view of the maintenance of water heating systems. It is caused by the bicarbonates of calcium and magnesium whereas 'permanent hardness' (hardness which cannot be removed by boiling) is caused by the dissolved sulphates and chlorides of these chemicals.

When water containing the bicarbonates of calcium and magnesium is heated to temperatures of about $160°F$ and above, carbon dioxide is driven off and the dissolved bicarbonates are changed into insoluble carbonates which are precipitated out as boiler scale or kettle fur. A glance into the inside of any domestic kettle will establish whether or not temporary hardness is a problem in that particular area. If it is, the electric element and the base and sides of the kettle will be coated with creamy white scale. This scale will not have formed only on the inside of the kettle where it can at least be readily seen. It will also be present in the boiler and flow and return pipes of any 'direct' hot water system (see Chapter 3) and adhering to the element of any electric immersion heater.

Scale acts as an insulator and prevents the heat of the boiler fire, or of the electric element, being transferred to the water in the boiler or cylinder. Loss of efficiency is often the first, and frequently unnoticed, indication of a scale build-up. Later, as scale continues to build up, hissing, bubbling and banging sounds will be heard as water is forced through ever-diminishing water channels. Unfortunately, scale does not only insulate the water from the heating effect of the fire or electric element. It also insulates the surface of the boiler, or of the element, from the cooling effect of the circulating water. Eventually the metal of the boiler will burn away until a leak develops or the electric immersion heater will overheat and fail.

Boiler scale, like the fur in the domestic kettle, can be removed by chemical means. The system is partially drained and a descaling chemical introduced into it via the cold water supply pipe to the hot water storage cylinder. After the introduction of the chemical the boiler is lit and the water encouraged to circulate between boiler and cylinder to enable the chemical to act upon the scale accumulation. This treatment must, needless to say, be followed by very thorough flushing.

Permanent hardness does not affect hot water systems in this way but it has other harmful effects. Both forms of hardness prevent soap from dissolving and lathering properly in water. Insoluble, sticky deposits of lime soap or scum are formed that leave dirty 'tide marks' round baths and wash basins, matt woollens and damage other clothing washed in the water. Evaporation of hard water leaves the chemicals of both permanent and temporary hardness behind to produce marks below the taps of baths, jammed ball-valves and clogged up shower sprinklers.

Treatment of hardness and its effects will depend upon the particular aspect of the effect of hardness that is causing concern in individual circumstances. If, for instance, the main concern is the protection of boilers and immersion heaters from scale there are a number of mechanical measures that can be taken.

(a) Check the setting of the thermostat of the immersion heater. In soft water areas it is usual to set the thermostat at 160°F. In hard water areas the setting should be 140°F. It is only when the temperature of water rises above 140°F, which is quite hot enough for domestic purposes, that scale begins to form.

(b) Endeavour to control boiler temperatures so that the water does not rise above 140°F. This should be practicable where gas or oil are used though solid fuel boilers are less easily controllable. A dial thermometer clamped to the boiler flow pipe will permit the water temperature to be noted.

Never allow the water in a domestic 'boiler' to boil.

(c) Convert a 'direct' hot water system to 'indirect' as suggested in Chapter 3. The water in the primary circuit of an indirect is used over and over again, only the minute losses from evaporation being made up from the feed and expansion tank.

Any given volume of water contains only a given quantity of scale producing chemicals. The scale from these chemicals is deposited when the system is first heated and after that no more scale can form.

Some scale may still form in the hot water storage cylinder. This is however of less importance as it will not impede circulation. Forming on the inside of the cylinder it will, in fact, act as a kind of internal lagging jacket and thus perform a useful purpose.

There is also a chemical means by which, without actually softening the water supply, scale formation can be prevented. Certain phosphates of sodium and calcium (sold commercially as Micromet), when released in minute quantities into a hard water supply, stabilise the chemicals of temporary hardness so that they do not precipitate out as scale when the water is heated.

Micromet is prepared in crystalline form. The usual method of introduction into a hot water system is to suspend the crystals, in a purpose made plastic basket, inside the cold water storage cistern, as close as possible to the ball-valve inlet (*Figure 10.1a*). The crystals will slowly dissolve and (for the average household) need to be renewed at six monthly intervals.

Micromet can also be used for the threshold treatment of water passing, direct from the main, to instantaneous gas or

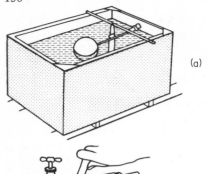

Fig. 10.1. Using Micromet to prevent scale formation: (a) by introducing it into the cold water storage cistern and (b) with a dispenser plumbed into the cold water supply pipe

(a)

1. Turn off water at main stop-cock. Fit 6 in (150 mm) of pipe to each side of dispenser head using compression joints and adaptors. Fit a stop valve to the outlet side of the head

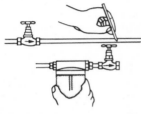

2. Using the dispenser as a guide, mask and cut the pipe. Remove the cut piece of pipe by undoing the stop-cock coupling

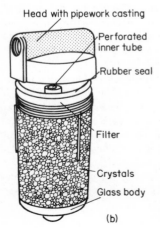

Head with pipework casting

Perforated inner tube

Rubber seal

Filter

Crystals

Glass body

(b)

3. Place the dispenser in position and secure with compression joints. With both cocks still closed, unscrew the dispenser body, fill with crystals and replace. Turn on both stopcocks and check for leaks

electric water heaters. A special container, filled with the crystals, is introduced into the pipe-line leading to the appliance (*Figure 10.1b*). It is, of course, essential to provide a stop-cock on either side of the Micromet container to enable the crystals to be renewed when required. Micromet, it must be stressed, does not *soften* water. Its purpose is to stabilise the chemicals that cause hardness and to prevent them from precipitating out as boiler scale when the water is heated.

Any domestic water supply can be softened completely— reduced to zero hardness—by the installation of a base exchange or, as they tend to be called nowadays, an ion exchange water softener. Water softeners of this kind are usually plumbed into the rising main so that every drop of water flowing into

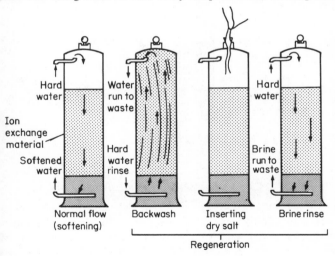

Fig. 10.2. The cycle of regeneration

the house is softened. Synthetic sodium compounds are used in modern base exchange water softeners but the principle was discovered by observing the way in which water could be softened by passage through a bed of natural zeolite sand.

The hard water chemicals 'exchange bases' with the water softening material. Calcium and magnesium are left in the softening material and *sodium* bicarbonate, which does not cause hardness, is to be found in small quantities in the water flowing out of the softener. After a period of time the water softening chemical becomes exhausted but can readily be reactivated by passing a solution of sodium chloride (common salt) through it (*Figure 10.2*). Complaints about mains water

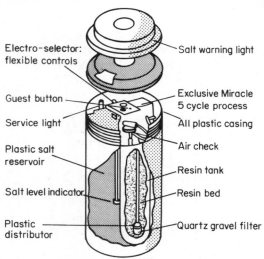

Electro-selector: flexible controls

Salt warning light

Guest button

Service light

Plastic salt reservoir

Salt level indicator

Plastic distributor

Exclusive Miracle 5 cycle process

All plastic casing

Air check

Resin tank

Resin bed

Quartz gravel filter

Fig. 10.3. Modern 'Sofnol Satum' automatic mains water softener

softeners usually relate to corrosion from frequent contact with salt water and to the rather tedious weekly task of reactivating the appliance with salt. Modern softeners overcome both of these objections. The body of the appliance is made of corrosion free plastic and the softener reactivates itself automatically from a large salt container at the prompting of a clock control (*Figure 10.3*).

Mains water softeners are somewhat expensive appliances and take up what may be considered to be an unacceptable amount of space in a compact modern home. They may too, be considered to be somewhat wasteful since they soften every drop of water passing into the home including, for instance, that used for w.c. flushing where soft water offers no advantage. Nor is soft water wholly without disadvantages. Many people consider that tea made with soft water is less palatable than that made with hard. Then too, a statistical relationship has been established between soft water supplies and the incidence of cardiovascular disease.

No-one really knows the reason for this. It *could* be that the chemicals responsible for hardness form a part of the body's natural defence mechanism against disease of this kind. It is more likely though that soft water's capacity to take into solution iron, copper or lead from the pipes through which it passes may be responsible. The first two of these metals are harmless enough if taken into the body in the tiny quantities likely to be found in a water supply.

Lead, on the other hand, is a dangerous and cumulative poison. Amounts well in excess of those considered to be acceptable have been found to be dissolved in water (in soft water areas) passing through lead pipes, particularly where water has stood in the pipes overnight. This need not deter the householder from installing a mains water softener or the water engineer from advising installation. Lead pipes are rarely, if ever, used in modern plumbing work. Where a water softener is installed into the lead pipework of an existing plumbing system it is probable that the internal surfaces of the pipes will have acquired an eggshell coating of scale that will prevent the lead going into solution.

To be absolutely safe there is perhaps something to be said for installing the mains softener into the rising main *after* the branch to the kitchen sink cold tap has been teed off. This will mean that softened water will be available for washing purposes and for the hot water system but will not be used for cooking and drinking. If a house has a naturally soft water supply the householder might be well advised to run off, every morning, the few pints of water that have been standing in the pipes overnight. Hot water dissolves metals more readily than cold. One should never be tempted, particularly first thing in the morning, to fill a kettle to make tea from the hot tap.

As well as the large mains base exchange water softeners already mentioned there are available small, portable softeners which can be used to supply limited quantities of softened water for hair washing, laundry purposes and so on (*Figure 10.4*). These small softeners operate on the base exchange

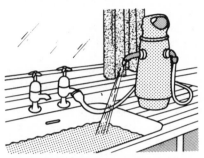

Fig. 10.4. Small portable water softener. This is coupled to the hot-water tap by a rubber hose and refilled with common salt after every 150 gallons of water

principle. They have a hose inlet with a connector suitable for pushing on to any domestic tap. A salt cap at the top of the appliance can be unscrewed to permit salt to be added for regeneration when required.

Small quantities of water can also be softened by the addition of chemicals to the water after it has been drawn off. Most of these chemicals, which are used (among other things) as bath salts, are based on washing soda. They have the effect of causing the chemicals causing hardness to become insoluble, precipitating out and leaving softened water behind. Disadvantages of these chemicals include the fact that the precipitate may harm clothing and the alkaline nature of the softened water can cause some dyes to run and may irritate sensitive skins.

Another chemical water softener, sodium hexametaphosphate (sold commercially as Calgon) works in a rather different way. This is a fine white powder, used straight from the packet, which when added to a hard water, links up with the chemicals causing hardness and neutralises them, so that they do not prevent soap from dissolving.

Calgon does not form a precipitate. Nor does it make the water alkaline. It can be used with confidence for laundry purposes, hair washing, washing and shaving—in fact for softening, for any purpose, any relatively small quantity of hard water.

11 Frost Precautions

Under normal atmospheric pressure water freezes and turns into ice at 0°C (32°F). As it freezes it expands, increasing its volume by between 9 and 10%. These two facts explain the importance of adequate frost protection in plumbing installation.

At the time of writing Great Britain has enjoyed a succession of extremely mild winters. Even so, there can be few parts of the country where air temperatures have not fallen below 0°C on at least some occasions during each year. Memory has to go back over little more than ten years to recall winters during which sub-zero temperatures and bitter north-easterly winds were maintained for days or weeks at a time.

Because a really hard winter is something of a rarity installers and householders tend to regard frost protection rather casually. Thus, when a prolonged freezing spell does occur, thousands of homes are without water and the thaw brings flooding from a thousand burst pipes. To many people frost protection simply means efficient lagging. Yet intelligent design and installation can do far more to prevent freeze-ups and burst pipes than any amount of lagging.

Some aspects of frost resistant plumbing design have been referred to briefly in earlier chapters. Frost rarely penetrates deeper than about 2ft into the soil in this country. The service pipe bringing water supply into the house from the main should therefore be at least 0.82m (2ft 6in) underground *throughout its length*. The last three words are stressed because it is by no means unknown for an enthusiastic landscape gardener to reduce the effective depth of the service pipe to 1ft 6in or less by constructing a sunken garden or sunken lawn above it.

If the service pipe rises into the house via an open sub-floor exposed to draughts from air-bricks, it should be threaded through the centre of a 6in (150mm) length of drainpipe packed with vermiculite chips. The service pipe or rising main should preferably rise up into the roof space via an internal wall. Where this cannot, or has not, been arranged this pipe should be thoroughly protected from the cold external wall.

Interposing a ½in (12mm) wooden slat between the pipe and the external wall would probably be sufficient protection so far as frost precautions alone are concerned but problems would then arise from the condensation of moisture from the warm, damp air of the kitchen onto this pipe. It is therefore better to protect the pipe both from frost and condensation by thorough lagging (*Figure 11.1*). Use an inorganic lagging material and make sure that it extends behind the pipe so as

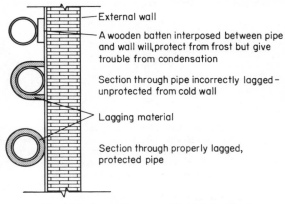

External wall

A wooden batten interposed between pipe and wall will protect from frost but give trouble from condensation

Section through pipe incorrectly lagged – unprotected from cold wall

Lagging material

Section through properly lagged, protected pipe

Fig. 11.1. Protecting water pipes against frost

to protect it from the cold wall. Foam plastic pipe lagging units, such as Armstrong 'Armaflex', are suitable for this purpose. New pipework can be threaded through these units as it is installed. Armaflex can also be used to protect existing pipework by slitting it and snapping it over the pipes (*Figure 11.2*).

It is best if the rising main can enter the roof space as far as possible from the eaves. If it rises against an outside wall it will enter the roof space in the immediate vicinity of the eaves where it will be exposed to draughts and inaccessible for thorough lagging and, if necessary, for thawing out.

Flexible foam plastic lagging is made to fit any pipe up to 3 in (75 mm) dia and is sold in 3 ft (914 mm) and 6 ft (1.8 m) lengths. It can be cut with sharp scissors. The lagging is fixed with waterproof plastic adhesive tape

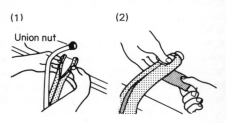

1. Starting at the tank, open the lagging and place it round the pipe and nut touching the tank wall. 2. Ensure that the edges are touching round the pipe and wrap adhesive tape round to secure the lagging

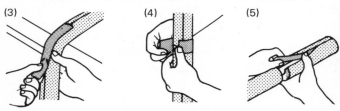

3. At the bends make sure the edges touch and seal lengthways with adhesive tape. 4. At joins in the lagging wrap adhesive tape overlapping both pieces of lagging so that there is no gap. 5. The final piece of lagging must be cut to fit exactly between the last piece and the wall. Use tape at the join and at the wall

Fig. 11.2. Lagging water pipes with foamed plastic

The roof space is a particularly vulnerable area so far as frost damage is concerned and plumbing installations in this area in a modern home with a conscientious and intelligent occupier may be at even greater risk than those in an older house with an occupier of a different kind.

In a modern home the bedroom ceilings will be insulated against heat loss by means of a fibreglass quilt or loose fill insulating material. The rooms below will be warmer but the roof space will be that much colder. There will be no escape of warmth from the rooms below to give the plumbing installation that little extra measure of protection during icy weather.

The roof space therefore demands special attention. The lengths of service pipe and distributing pipes within this area should be kept as short as possible and should be particularly thoroughly lagged. The bodies of ball-valves, gate valves and any other control valves should not be overlooked. These too should be thoroughly lagged so that only the handles or heads protrude from the lagging. Do not omit to lag the vent pipe of the hot water system. It will be filled with water to the same level as that of the water in the storage cistern.

The means of protecting the cold water storage cistern from both frost and contamination have been discussed in Chapter 2. If the house has a solid fuel boiler for a hot water or central heating system the storage cistern is best situated against the flue serving this boiler. Ideally, the boiler, hot water storage cylinder and cold water storage cistern should be arranged in a vertical column so that there will be a continuous flow of warm air upwards towards the vulnerable cistern. Prevent cold draughts from entering the roof space via the overflow or warning pipe by turning the internal end over, as suggested in Chapter 2, so that it dips an inch or so below water level when the cistern is full.

In a modern, effectively heated and thermally insulated home, no special precautions need to be taken for the protection of water distribution pipes below the level of the roof space. They should be kept away from external walls or, where this unavoidable, thoroughly lagged.

It is largely as a frost protection measure that the Building Regulations require waste and soil pipes to be contained within the fabric of the building. Where a house has external waste and soil pipes the important point to remember is that an empty pipe cannot freeze. Every householder's routine autumn frost precautions should include the renewal of the washers of any taps showing a tendency to drip. A waste pipe, dripping all night into an exposed hopper head, can produce a hopper

head and down-pipe choked solid with ice on the morning
following a night of severe frost.

Lagging, however thorough and efficient, cannot *add* heat
to the plumbing system. It can only reduce the rate of heat
loss. Careful positioning of the storage cistern above the hot
water cylinder can actually add heat to the system. This too
can be done in other ways. Lagging units incorporating a
low power electric heating cable can be bound round vulnerable pipes and switched on when severe frost threatens.
It may be possible to protect the flushing cistern of an external
w.c. by thoroughly draught proofing the compartment and
then, by means of an extension lead plugged into the electric
light socket, suspending a 60 watt electric light bulb outside
the cistern a few inches below the ball valve inlet (*Figure 11.3*).

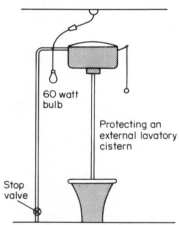

*Fig. 11.3 Protecting an external
lavatory cistern*

Under more or less draught free conditions the heat generated
by a bulb of this kind will be sufficient to afford protection
from quite a severe degree of frost.

The fact that lagging does no more than reduce the rate of
heat loss must be borne in mind when a house is unoccupied

for more than a few days during severe winter weather. Continued occupation of a dwelling and continued use of its plumbing system are, in themselves, important safeguards against frost damage. The interior of the house is maintained at temperatures well above freezing point and this warmth is transmitted to the water pipes contained within it. Water enters the house from the main at a temperature a few degrees above freezing point. In the roof space it may begin to cool down but, before it can reach danger level, it is drawn off through the taps or flushing cisterns and replaced by marginally warmer water from the main.

The fabric of an empty, unheated house quickly chills off. Water stagnates in the supply and distributing pipes and in the storage cisterns. During a prolonged spell of freezing weather—no matter how thoroughly the pipes are lagged—an ice plug will eventually form and spread through the system. If a house has a *reliable* automatic central heating system the best course of action is to leave this system on, low, partially removing the trap door to the roof space to permit some warm air to circulate there.

The only other safe alternative is to drain the system completely. The method of drainage will depend upon the design of the particular plumbing installation but, where a house has a cylinder storage hot water system as described in Chapter 3 of this book, the following procedure should be followed.

Turn off the householder's main stop-cock and drain the rising main from the drain-cock immediately above it. Open up all taps and leave open after they have drained. Ice plugs may form in undrainable lengths of pipe leading to, for instance, the bathroom taps. However, so long as the taps are left open, the expansion of these ice plugs can be accommodated longitudinally towards the open ends of the pipe and there need be no lateral expansion to cause damage.

The hot water storage cylinder cannot be drained from the hot water taps, nor can the primary circuit of any indirect system whether or not used in conjunction with a central heating system. Drain from the drain-cock beside the boiler, using a garden hose with the open end taken to an external gully. An indirect cylinder, or a direct cylinder heated by an immersion heater only, must also be drained from the drain-cock that will probably be provided on the cold water inlet to the cylinder. Any central heating circuit will probably have other drain-cocks provided at low points and these too should be drained.

After draining leave a large and conspicuous notice on the boiler to the effect that the system has been drained and that the boiler should on no account be lit before it has been refilled with water.

Refilling after drainage can produce troubles from air-locks. Leave all taps and radiator vent valves open until water starts to flow through them. It is often helpful to refill by connecting one end of a length of hose to the cold tap over the kitchen sink and the other end to the boiler drain-cock. Open up the tap and the drain-cock and the system will fill *upwards,* driving air in front of the rising water.

Do not omit to flush the w.c. cistern or cisterns before leaving the house. Water in w.c. traps and other traps must not, of course, be drained off. Throwing a handful of salt

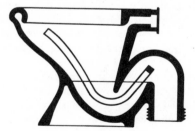

*Fig. 11.4. Rubber tube with stoppered
end passed through w.c. trap*

into the water in the traps will generally afford adequate protection. A more positive means of protection for the vulnerable w.c. trap is to fix a stopper into the end of a length of rubber tubing and pass the stoppered end into and round the w.c. trap (*Figure 11.4*). If the water in the trap freezes and expands the expansion will then be accommodated by the rubber tubing.

If a freeze-up occurs

The first indication that water has frozen in the plumbing system of an occupied house will be the failure of water to flow from one or more of the taps or into the w.c. flushing cistern.

At first the ice plug will be a small one, easily dealt with. Action should be taken quickly to prevent stagnation of cold water in the pipe affected and the inevitable growth of the plug.

Identify, as accurately as possible, the point at which the blockage has taken place. If, for instance, water is flowing freely from the cold tap over the kitchen sink but is not flowing into the cold water storage cistern, the ice plug will be in the rising main, probably within the roof space.

Strip off the lagging and apply cloths, wrung out in hot water, or a hot water bottle, to this pipe. Modern copper tubing is a good conductor of heat and application of heat in the way suggested will thaw a small ice plug several feet from the point of application. An electric hair dryer, or even a vacuum cleaner operating in reverse, can prove useful in directing a stream of warm air to an otherwise inaccessible pipe.

Dealing with a burst pipe

The idea persists that pipes burst with the thaw. This is, of course, incorrect. Pipes burst when they freeze, but the burst only becomes evident when the ice thaws and water can flow again.

The first indication of a burst is usually water dripping from a ceiling or into an airing cupboard. Rapid and intelligent action by the householder immediately this occurs can limit the damage and save furniture and furnishings from being spoiled.

Immediately the householder should turn off the main stop-cock and open up all the taps in the house. This will cut off the water supply to the house and drain the storage cistern. There is no need to put out the boiler fire though it might be wise to keep it as low as possible. The hot water storage cylinder will still be full of water. Only after taking this action should the householder seek out the point at which the burst has occurred and consider the remedy.

If the house has copper plumbing joined with compression or soldered capillary joints, the chances are that the 'burst' will merely be the result of one of these joints having pulled apart. The joint can be remade simply and easily as described in the next chapter.

Copper tubing may sometimes split under internal pressure from expanding ice. A burst in a lead pipe will almost certainly take the form of a split. It must be mentioned that house-holders are sometimes led into a state of false security by the fact that a lead pipe may have frozen on a number of occasions and has never burst. Each time the pipe has frozen the ice plug, on expanding, will have increased the bore of the pipe—and reduced the thickness of the pipe walls. Since lead lacks elasticity the pipe will not resume its former dimensions on thawing out. This process may be repeated several times before internal pressure finally splits the pipe wall.

The remedy in the case of a split pipe is to cut out the damaged section of the pipe and replace it with a new length. If the pipe is of lead the new length will be connected to the old by means of two wiped soldered joints. The technique of making a joint of this kind is described in the next chapter but it does require considerable practice and will certainly be beyond the capacity of an inexperienced householder in an emergency. Professional help should be obtained.

However a temporary repair can be made with the use of one of the epoxy resin fillers such as Isopon or Plastic Padding. The edges of the split should be knocked together and the area thoroughly dried and cleaned with abrasive paper. The

filler is then made up according to the manufacturer's instructions and buttered round the area of the split. Before setting a
length of fibreglass bandage is bound round the area affected
and a further layer of filler applied to the fibreglass bandage.

Boiler explosion and cylinder collapse

Any period of prolonged severe weather produces at least one
report in the national press of fatalities from a boiler explosion. This creates a great deal of anxiety among householders, particularly the elderly who will sometimes take the
'precaution' of letting the boiler fire out during frosty weather
—the worst possible course of action under the circumstances.

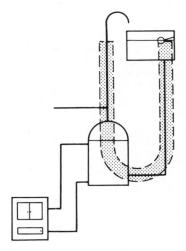

Fig. 11.5. The open ended U-tube
formed by a hot water system

Boiler explosions are, happily, extremely rare. It is, after all,
'the exception that makes the news', as any journalist will
confirm. When they *do* occur their results can be catastrophic.

An understanding of their cause should do a great deal to allay totally unnecessary anxiety.

A cylinder storage hot water system, whether direct or indirect, resembles a U tube, with two open ends—a larger version of the kind of U tube found in every school physics or chemistry laboratory. The two ends, open to the atmosphere, are the vent pipe and the cold water storage cistern (*Figure 11.5*). Provided either one of these ends remains open and unobstructed, no boiler explosion can take place. A spring loaded safety valve, situated close to the boiler in most hot water and central heating systems, provides a final line of defence.

Typically, boiler explosions take place when a family has been absent from home during a prolonged cold spell, without

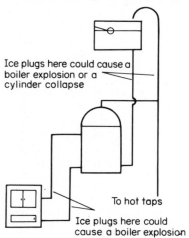

Fig. 11.6. Formation of ice plugs may cause cylinder collapse or a boiler explosion

taking the precautions suggested earlier in this chapter. Ice plugs have formed in the flow and return pipes between boiler and cylinder or in the upper part of the vent pipe and the upper part of the cold water supply pipe to the cylinder

(*Figure 11.6*). The boiler fire is lit but, of course, the water in the boiler can neither circulate nor expand upon heating.

Boiling depends upon temperature and pressure. The temperature of the water in the boiler rises to above 100°C but the water cannot, because it is confined within the boiler, turn to steam. Pressure increases until, ultimately, something gives. In an instant the superheated water in the boiler is converted to steam, occupying thousands of times more space than the equivalent volume of water. The system explodes like a bomb with catastrophic results.

Cylinder implosion or collapse is rather more common. It can occur where pipework in the roof space is inadequately lagged and where the householder, perhaps through fear of a boiler explosion, has let the boiler fire out at night during icy weather. A small ice plug forms in the vent pipe and in the upper part of the cold supply pipe to the hot water cylinder. Meanwhile the water stored in the cylinder, originally hot, cools—and contracts.

Copper hot water cylinders are constructed to withstand considerable internal pressure but very little external pressure. As the cooling water contracts a partial vacuum is created within the cylinder and it collapses like a paper bag under the weight of the atmosphere. Typically, cylinder implosion occurs first thing in the morning when the householder turns on the hot tap to draw off some water. The additional loss of water proves to be the final straw that breaks the camel's back.

The best safeguards against boiler explosion, cylinder collapse and, indeed, all troubles arising from frost, are intelligent lagging, particularly in the roof space, keeping the boiler fire alight and the house warm during frosty weather and draining the system completely if the house is left unoccupied for more than a few days during a period when icy weather might reasonably be expected.

12 Materials and Methods

Many plumbing textbooks begin with a study of the materials used by the plumber and the means by which pipes and fittings of these materials are joined together. It is the author's opinion that, for the beginner at any rate, this is the wrong approach. The student of plumbing, whether he hopes to become a professional plumber or is 'merely' an intelligent householder, first needs to familiarise himself with the principles of water supply and drainage. Only when he has thoroughly mastered these principles should he attempt the practice by which they are put into effect.

Plumbing practice, so far as it relates to domestic water supply and drainage, consists of the means of manipulating pipework of different materials and connecting these pipes to others of the same or different material or to plumbing fittings such as taps, ball valves, cisterns and cylinders.

Materials used in plumbing installations today include copper and its alloys, stainless steel, galvanised steel and iron, lead and its alloys, pitch-fibre and a variety of plastics.

Copper

Copper is one of the most versatile and easily handled modern plumbing materials. It is used for water supply pipes, hot water storage cylinders and for waste drainage. Alloys of copper, brass and gunmetal are used for the manufacture of taps, stop-valves, ball-valves and indeed, all plumbing joints and fittings.

Copper tubing used for domestic water supply and central heating is supplied in 'half hard' and 'dead soft' temper. Half hard temper tubing is obtainable in straight lengths and is the kind generally used for above-ground water services. Dead soft temper copper tubing is sold in long coils and is particularly useful for underground service pipes where joints, potential points of leakage, are undesirable. Dead soft copper tubing is also used in microbore central heating as it can easily be threaded through and under floorboards to make for unobtrusive installation.

The commonest means of jointing copper tubing for domestic water supply and waste drainage are by the use of non-manipulative (Type 'A') compression joints, manipulative (Type 'B') compression joints or by means of soldered capillary joints. All these joints are easily made with a minimal tool kit suitable for both professional and amateur use.

Joints and fittings for use with copper tubing may be made either of brass (an alloy of copper and zinc) or of gunmetal (an alloy of copper and tin). Joints and fittings of the latter material are recommended in areas where the water supply has corrosive characteristics and the phenomenon known as 'dezincification' is liable to occur. Dezincification is a form of electrolytic corrosion which results in the zinc of the brass alloy dissolving away to produce a fitting, unchanged in external appearance, but totally without structural strength.

Non-manipulative (Type A) compression joints and fittings

These provide the simplest, though not the least expensive, means of joining copper tubing and connecting to it fittings such as stop-cocks, taps and ball-valves.

A Type A compression joint comprises a joint body, a cap nut and a soft copper ring or 'olive' (*Figures 12.1* and *12.2*). To connect a compression joint to one end of a length of copper tubing the procedure is as follows (*Figure 12.3*).

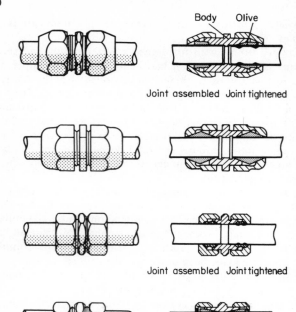

Fig. 12.1. Non-manipulative (Type A) compression couplings

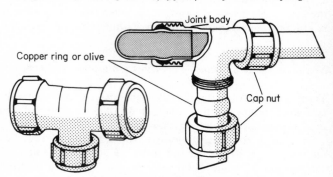

Fig. 12.2. A Conex Type A compression tee joint

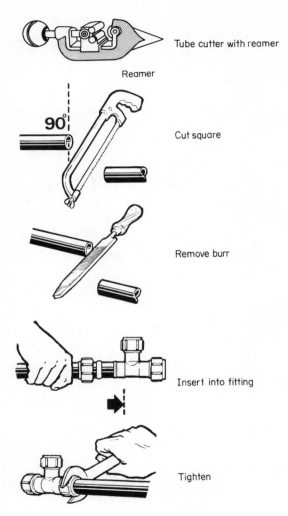

Tube cutter with reamer

Reamer

Cut square

Remove burr

Insert into fitting

Tighten

Fig. 12.3. Making a Conex compression joint

172

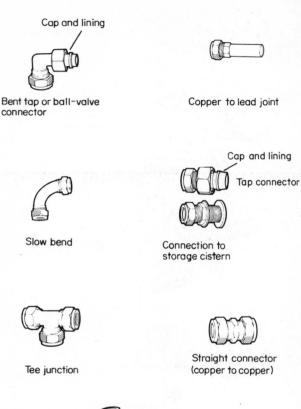

Cap and lining

Bent tap or ball-valve
connector

Copper to lead joint

Slow bend

Cap and lining

Tap connector

Connection to
storage cistern

Tee junction

Straight connector
(copper to copper)

—Tail of bib tap
screw in here

Wall plate elbow for
outside tap

Fig. 12.4. Some Prestex compression fittings

Cut the tube end square and remove all trace of internal and external burr. This operation can be done with a hacksaw and a file but, where a number of joints are to be made, the use of a wheel tube cutter, preferably incorporating a reamer to remove internal burr, will save time and ensure a squarely cut end every time.

Some manufacturers recommend that, in order to make the joint, the cap nut, followed by the olive, should be slipped separately over the pipe and this end thrust into the body of the joint as far as the pipe stop. Others say that there is no need to dismantle their joints before making them. Simply loosen the cap nut and push the tube end home. In either case the tube end must be pushed in to the pipe stop and the cap nut tightened. This action compresses the olive against the outer wall of the tube to make a watertight joint.

Tighten with the fingers and complete the tightening process with a spanner. Provided that a spanner, rather than a wrench, is used, it is virtually impossible to overtighten. Most professional plumbers smear a little boss white or other waterproofing compound over the tube end and the interior of the compression joint before making the joint. Although this should not be necessary it does accommodate any unevenness in the tube and ensures a watertight joint at the first attempt.

Manufacturers of Type 'A' compression joints publish illustrated catalogues of their products which show the very wide range of fittings available (*Figure 12.4*). Stop-cocks and drain-cocks are made with compression inlets and outlets for direct connection to pipes. There are also easy and knuckle bends, equal and reducing tees for inserting branch pipe lines, fittings with compression inlets and cap and lining outlets for connection to taps and ball-valves and fittings with compression inlets and threaded outlets, male or female, for connection to cylinders, cisterns and pipes of materials other than copper.

Manipulative (Type B) compression joints and fittings

These differ from Type A joints in that the tube end has to be 'worked' or manipulated and is itself an integral part of the completed joint.

174

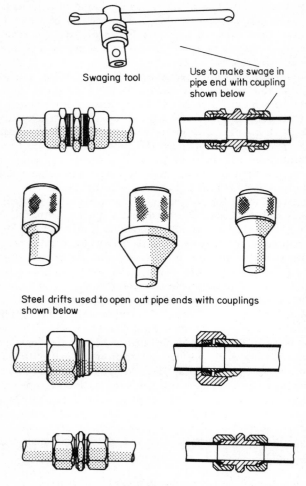

Swaging tool

Use to make swage in pipe end with coupling shown below

Steel drifts used to open out pipe ends with couplings shown below

Fig. 12.5. Manipulative (Type B) compression couplings

To make a Type B joint the tube end must first be cut squarely and all burr removed as with a Type A joint. The cap nut must then be unscrewed from the joint and slipped over the tube end. *After* this has been done the tube end must be manipulated (*Figure 12.5*).

This is usually done by hammering in a steel drift to expand the tube end. However, one well-known make of Type B joint (the Kingley, made by the Kings Langley Engineering Co.) requires the tube end to be manipulated in a rather different way. A special 'swaging tool' is inserted into the pipe end and turned. Turning this tool forces a hard steel ball to make a ridge or 'swage' round the pipe end. The pipe is then placed against or into the body of the joint as the case may be and the cap nut screwed on and tightened. It is wise to apply boss white to the pipe end when making a Type B joint.

As can be seen, once the pipe end has been manipulated, the cap nut cannot be removed. This means that the pipe is much more positively secured than with a Type A joint. The joint cannot pull apart as a result of ground settlement or expansion of ice. For this reason Water Authorities usually insist upon the use of Type B joints for underground work. A disadvantage, which is probably not a serious one in most situations, is that the joint cannot be dismantled as easily as a Type A joint.

Soldered capillary joints and fittings

The effect of capillary action—the property of liquids that causes them to flow into any confined space between two solid surfaces—can be demonstrated by means of a simple experiment. Take two pieces of glass, separate them by about 1½mm ($^1/_{16}$ in) and dip their edges into a vessel filled with coloured water. The water will be observed to flow upwards to fill the space between the two sheets of glass.

Capillarity has its disadvantages. It is, for instance, the cause of rising damp in buildings. The plumber however can take advantage of it. The effectiveness of soldered capillary joints depends upon the fact that molten solder, like water, will flow to fill any confined space between two solid surfaces.

Soldered capillary joints and fittings are smaller, cheaper and less obtrusive than compression joints and fittings. They are scarcely more difficult to make though a blow torch is, of course, an essential.

There are two kinds of capillary joint—the integral ring and the end-feed (*Figure 12.6*). Integral ring capillary joints (often called Yorkshire fittings after the name of one well-known brand) incorporate sufficient solder to make the joint.

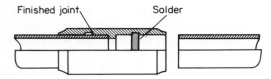

Fig. 12.6. Integral ring soldered capillary joint. End-feed fittings are identical but have no ring of solder

Preparation of the tube end begins as with a compression joint. Cut the end dead square and remove all burr. Next clean the end of the tube, and the internal bore of the capillary fitting, thoroughly with steel wool or fine abrasive paper. Apply an approved flux to both these surfaces (*Figure 12.7*). Thrust the tube end into the fitting as far as the tube stop. Apply the flame of a blow torch, first to the pipe in the vicinity of the fitting and then to the fitting itself. The solder in the integral ring will melt and flow to fill the narrow space between tube and fitting. The joint is made when a bright ring of solder appears all round the mouth of the fitting. It should then be left undisturbed until cool enough to touch.

Solder wire is used to feed solder into the cheaper end-feed fittings. About ½in of wire is needed for a 15mm fitting, ¾in for a 22mm one and 1in for a 28mm one. It can be helpful to bend this length of wire over before beginning the operation. Cut, clean and flux as before and apply the blow torch flame to the tube end and fitting. Feed in the solder when flux can

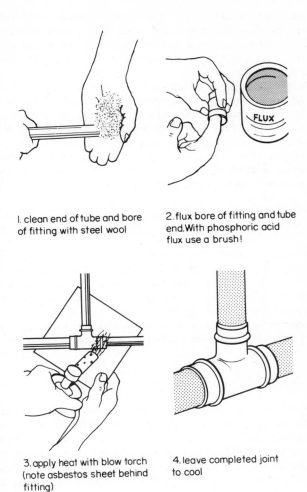

1. clean end of tube and bore of fitting with steel wool

2. flux bore of fitting and tube end. With phosphoric acid flux use a brush!

3. apply heat with blow torch (note asbestos sheet behind fitting)

4. leave completed joint to cool

Fig. 12.7. Making a 'Yorkshire' integral ring soldered capillary joint

be seen to be boiling at the mouth of the fitting. The joint is complete when all the bent over piece of wire has been melted and fed into the fitting and, as with an integral ring joint, when a ring of bright solder appears round the mouth of the fitting.

Where more than one joint is to be made to a fitting, as in a straight coupling or a tee connection, it is best if both or all joints can be made at the same time. If this is impossible a piece of damp cloth whould be wrapped round joints already made to prevent the solder in them from melting.

Always remember the fire risk when using a blow torch. Interpose a sheet of asbestos or a piece of fibreglass between the joint and any wooden, or plastic, surface in the vicinity.

Other jointing methods

Other means which may be used by the professional plumber for jointing copper tubing include silver or hard soldering and bronze welding. These methods involve the application of considerably more heat than can be obtained from a conventional blow lamp or blow torch. For bronze welding oxy-acetelene apparatus is required and the techniques involved are not considered suitable for a beginner's guide.

Metrication

Imperial sizes of copper tubes in common use in domestic plumbing are: $^3/_8$ in, ½in, ¾in, 1in, 1¼in, 1½in and 2in. Metric equivalent sizes are: 12mm, 15mm, 22mm, 28mm, 35mm, 42mm and 54mm. These equivalents are not exact translations of Imperial into metric measurements. The reason for this is that Imperial measurements of copper tubing are of the *internal* diameter. Metric measurements are of the *external* diameter of the tube.

When connecting new metric tubing to existing Imperial sized tubing 12mm, 15mm, 28mm and 54mm compression joints can be used, without adaptation with $^3/_8$ in, ½in, 1in and 2in tube. Adaptors are required for the connection of ¾in, 1¼in and 1½in Imperial tube to 22mm, 35mm and 42mm metric tubing. These adaptors are readily available.

Capillary joints demand a much more critical fit than compression joints and, where new metric tubing is to be connected to existing Imperial sized tubing by means of capillary joints, an adaptor should always be used. An alternative, where $^3/_8$ in, ½in, 1in or 2in tubing is concerned, is to deal with any metric extension by using a compression joint for the actual connection between Imperial and metric tubing and then to continue the job using capillary joints.

Bending copper tubing

All manufacturers of compression and capillary joints and fittings include a variety of bends within their range of products. Easy bends can however be made in copper tubing either by hand or with the aid of a bending machine and use of this technique can provide a neater, and considerably cheaper, installation.

If a piece of copper tubing is simply bent over the knee it will be noted that the inside or throat of the bend is kinked and the outside or back is flattened while, at the bend, the tube will be elliptical instead of circular in section. To prevent this from occurring the walls of the tube must be supported as the bend is made.

One way of doing this is by means of a bending spring. Steel bending springs are made for all sizes of copper tube. They have an eyelet in the end into which a tommy bar can be inserted. Alternatively, where the bend is to be made in the middle of a length of pipe an extension rod can be hooked into this eyelet.

The spring should be greased to facilitate easy withdrawal and inserted into the tube to the point at which the bend is to be made (*Figure 12.8*). The tube is then bent over the knee, overbending by a few degrees at first and then bringing back to

the required curve. To withdraw the spring insert a tommy bar
into the eyelet, twist to reduce the diameter of the spring, and
pull.

Bending spring inserted

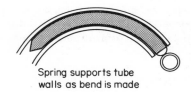

Spring supports tube
walls as bend is made

*Fig. 12.8. Bending copper tube with the aid of a
bending spring*

*Fig. 12.9. Small hand bending
machine*

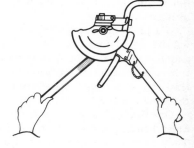

A bending machine provides an alternative means of bending
copper tubing and will probably be preferred by the professional (*Figure 12.9*). The essential difference between
spring and machine bending is the fact that in spring bending
the walls of the tube are supported internally, while a bending
machine provides external support.

Easy bends in small diameter copper tubing may be made cold. For sharper bends or for easy bends in large diameter pipe, sand or lead loading may be necessary to support the walls and the metal of the tube may need to be annealed— heated to a red heat to change the temper of the copper from half-hard to soft.

Stainless steel

Stainless steel is widely accepted as a first class material for the manufacture of sinks and other kitchen equipment. Although stainless steel tubing has been available in this country for over a decade as an alternative to copper tubing it has not earned the popularity that it deserves.

Stainless steel tubing is obtainable in the same sizes as copper tubing. It can be used in any situation where copper could be used and in some situations where it would be unwise to use copper.

In Chapter 2 reference was made to the danger of electrolytic corrosion that arises where galvanised steel and copper are used in one plumbing system. There is no such risk involved in the use of stainless steel. This material can be used in conjunction with copper tubing or, provided that it is not already rusting, old galvanised steel plumbing. It is therefore the obvious choice when extensions are planned for an existing galvanised steel plumbing system. Stainless steel, as a home product, has a relatively stable price that compares favourably with that of copper tubing.

Like copper tubing, stainless steel tubing may be joined with either Type A or Type B compression joints or by means of soldered capillary joints. There are however one or two points that should be noted when jointing stainless steel tubing. Although a wheel tube cutter can be used with stainless steel tubing this material is best cut with a high speed hacksaw blade having 32 teeth per inch. This is especially important if Type B compression fittings are to be used. A tube cutter will work harden the tube ends and make them liable to split when manipulated. Stainless steel is a harder material than copper. For this reason a little more pressure may be required when tightening the cap nut of a compression joint to ensure a watertight joint.

When using capillary fittings with stainless steel tube a phosphoric acid, *not a chloride,* based flux should be used. The supplier of the tubing should be able to suggest a suitable flux. The flux should be applied to the tube end and the interior of the fitting with a brush, not with the fingers. In making a capillary joint with stainless steel tubing a gentle flame from the blow torch should be applied to the fitting itself, not to the tube. As with copper tubing the joint is complete when a ring of bright solder appears round the mouth of the fitting.

Stainless steel tubing is less easily bent than copper tubing. Tubing of up to 22mm diameter can be bent using a bending machine. Spring bending is suitable for tubing of 15mm diameter or less.

Screwed iron and steel pipes and fittings

Because of their weight, clumsy appearance and the fact that they cannot be bent, screwed iron and steel tubing, usually protected against corrosion by galvanising, are rarely if ever used in new plumbing work today.

These materials were however in common use between about 1920 and 1940. It is not unusual to find pre-war sub-urban homes with hot and cold water systems wholly of galvanised steel—cold water storage cistern, hot water storage tank, flow and return pipes and distribution pipes. It may therefore be required for replacement or extension work. Pipes of this kind have threaded ends and are joined by means of the screwed fittings illustrated (*Figure 12.10*). To ensure watertight joints p.t.f.e. plastic thread sealing tape should be bound round the male thread before it is screwed home.

It not infrequently happens that the galvanised steel hot water storage tank of a hot water system constructed of this material fails through corrosion while the remainder of the system is still sound. In this event the temptation to replace the tank with a modern copper hot water storage cylinder should be resisted unless it is proposed, at the same time, to replace the galvanised steel tubing that comprises the remainder of the system with either copper or stainless steel tubing. The risk of electrolytic corrosion is even greater in hot water systems than in cold systems.

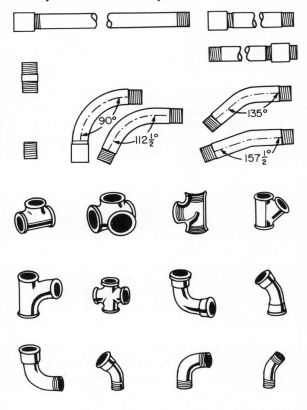

Fig. 12.10. Examples of screwed iron pipes and fittings

The metrication of iron and steel tubing has resulted in rather less confusion than has the metrication of copper and stainless steel tubing. Measurements are still of the internal diameter. The equivalents are set out below:

Imperial size	Metric equivalent
$^{3}/_{8}$ in	10mm
½in	12mm
¾in	20mm
1in	25mm
1¼in	32mm
1½in	40mm
2in	50mm

For all practical purposes there is no change between the sizes of Imperial iron and steel tubing and their metric equivalents. The British Standard Pipe (BSP) thread form has now been accepted internationally and its dimensions will not change. This, of course, relates to the tails of taps and ball valves as well as to iron pipe fittings.

Lead pipes

Lead is the traditional plumbing material. It is, of course, from its Latin name that the word plumbing is derived. Its expense, and the expertise and experience that is needed to handle it efficiently, ensures that it is never nowadays used for new hot or cold water services or drainage. There are however a great many lead, or partially lead, plumbing systems in existence. The professional plumber at least, must know how to cope with lead pipe for replacement and maintenance work.

Lead pipes are joined together by means of a wiped soldered joint. In the introduction it was stated that the technique of making such a joint is far easier to describe that to put into practice. The beginner will probably need to make several attempts before he produces a wiped soldered joint of which he can feel proud. He may console himself with the thought that it is a skill, like riding a bicycle, which, once acquired, is never lost. Before examining the technique, we should look at the properties of solder.

Solder is an alloy of lead and tin, and a small percentage of antimony. Its value lies in the fact that it has a lower melting

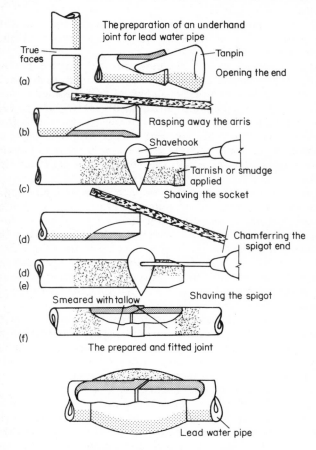

Fig. 12.11. Making a wiped soldered joint

point that any of the elements of which it is composed. Hence the fact that it can be used to join lead pipe without the risk of the lead itself softening and becoming deformed. Solder used with the soldered capillary joints discussed earlier in this chapter has a relatively high percentage of tin and a low melting point—between 170 and 190°C or 340 and 370°F. Plumber's wiping solder on the other hand contains roughly two parts of lead to one of tin and has an appreciably higher melting point—230°C or 440°F.

Careful preparation of the pipe ends is the first important step in the making of a good wiped soldered joint. Ends should be cut squarely and cleaned of all burr. A socket is then formed in one pipe in a tanpin, or hardwood cone (*Figure 12.11*). The external edge, or 'arris', of this opened-out end is then rasped away. The other pipe end is formed into a spigot by rasping to the angle of taper of the tanpin. This will ensure that it fits closely into the socket prepared in the other pipe end.

To limit the extent of the completed joint each pipe end is now coated with tarnish or plumber's black, to which molten solder will not adhere. Mark the limit of the joint on both spigot and socket ends and, with a shavehook, shave away the tarnish *and the surface coating of lead oxide* from the area of the joint, leaving bright, bare metal exposed. The cleaned surfaces must immediately be protected from further oxidation by smearing with tallow. Assemble the joint and fix firmly for wiping.

There may still be some traditional plumbers who make wiped joints with a solder pot and ladle, splashing molten solder onto upright joints with a splash stick and moulding into shape with a wiping cloth. Most modern plumbers prefer to use the solder stick method which is easier, safer and can produce just as satisfactory results.

The flame of a blow torch is applied to the lead pipe on each side of the joint, slowly traversing to and fro until the lead has reached a temperature above that of the melting point of solder. Rub the solder stick lightly onto the shaved surface of the lead pipe so that it 'tins' the entire surface and runs, by capillary attraction, into the confined space between the spigot and socket of the joint.

As more heat is applied the solder stick will soften and blobs of solder will be released. These must be built up round the joint with the moleskin wiping cloth to a neat finish.

The length of a wiped soldered joint will depend upon the sizes of the pipes being joined.

Internal bore	Length	Internal bore	Length
10mm	70mm	40mm	75mm
12mm	70mm	65mm	80mm
20mm	70mm	75mm	90mm
25mm	75mm	100mm	90mm
32mm	75mm		

As with galvanised iron and steel tubing, lead tubing is still designated by its internal diameter and there is no change, for all practical purposes, between the sizes of Imperial lead tubing and their metric equivalents.

The wiped soldered joint described is most likely to be needed in connection with the replacement of a burst or leaking length of existing lead pipework. This should be a relatively rare occurrence.

What the modern plumber is more likely to need is a means of connecting new copper or stainless steel tubing to existing lead pipe. This situation frequently arises in modernisation and improvement work. An obsolete and leaking lead plumbing system has been ripped out and a new copper or stainless steel system is to be installed. The first task is to connect copper tubing to a cut-off length of lead tubing projecting from the floor boards.

All manufacturers of compression and capillary joints and fittings include lead-to-copper connectors within their range of products. There is no difficulty in connecting the copper end of the connector to the copper or stainless steel tube. The lead end has to be connected to the lead tube by means of a wiped soldered joint similar to that described above. The projecting end of lead tube will form the 'socket' of the new joint (*Figure 12.12a*). It must be opened up with a tanpin, rasped and cleaned as though another length of lead pipe were to be connected to it.

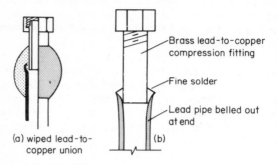

(a) wiped lead-to-copper union

Brass lead-to-copper compression fitting

Fine solder

Lead pipe belled out at end

(b)

Fig. 12.12. Joining copper compression fittings to lead pipe

The lead end of the lead-to-copper union must now be prepared. Its tail must be thoroughly scored with a medium cut file to remove the dull coating of chemical impurities arising from oxidation. The filed portion must be lightly smeared with tallow and plumber's black applied to the other end of the fitting to mark the limit of the joint.

The scored end of the union must then be 'tinned'. This means covering with a coat of fine general purpose solder, composed of equal parts of lead and tin. The solder is best applied to the tail of the union with a large copper bit. When the union has been tinned its end is placed into the socket of the lead pipe and secured with wooden splints. The wiped soldered joint is then made as previously described.

A simpler copper to lead connection can be made with a cup-and-cone joint (*Figure 12.12b*). This is acceptable for waste pipes and gas fittings but cannot be used for pipes carrying water under pressure. The end of the lead pipe is belled out by driving in a hardwood cone or turn-pin until the spigot end of the union can be accommodated to a depth equal to about half of its diameter. The spigot end of the union is rasped and tinned and fixed firmly into the lead socket. Fine solder is then run into the cup, the space between the union spigot and the lead socket, to fill it.

Polythene

Polythene may be used in plumbing for cold water storage cisterns and feed and expansion tanks. It may also be used for cold water supply and distribution pipes and was one of the first plastics to be used for this purpose. Polythene tubing is obtainable in long coils. It can easily be connected to copper tubing and has a built-in resistance to frost.

Its disadvantages are its thick, clumsy appearance and its tendency to sag which necessitates continuous support on horizontal runs. It cannot be used for hot water under pressure but is suitable for waste pipes taking warm wastes from baths, sinks and basins. Its chief value is as an easy and relatively cheap means of taking an underground water supply to a point distant from the home. It can be used to provide a garage supply or to supply a stand-tap at the end of a large garden.

The long lengths in which it is obtainable eliminate underground joints and it can be brought above the surface of the ground to supply a stand-tap without special frost precautions being taken. Polythene is a poor conductor or heat and cold and will provide a considerable measure of frost resistance. If the water in a polythene pipe *does* freeze the pipe will not burst. Polythene has sufficient resilience to accommodate the expansion of the ice and will revert to its original size when the ice thaws. These considerations make polythene tubing extremely valuable to, for instance, the proprietor of a caravan or camping site who must take a water supply to stand-pipes at various points throughout the site.

Polythene tubing is joined by non-manipulative compression joints and fittings similar to those used with copper tubing. Because polythene is a relatively soft material, a metal insert, provided by the manufacturer of the fitting, must be fitted into the tube end to prevent collapse when the cap-nut is tightened (*Figure 12.13*). Unscrew the cap-nut of the compression joint and slip it, followed by the olive, over the end of the tube. Push the metal insert into the end of the tube. Insert the tube end into the body of the fitting as far as the tube stop and tighten up the cap-nut. Tighten as far as possible with the fingers and then give a further one and a half to two turns with a spanner.

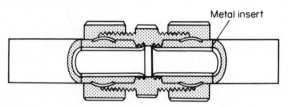

Fig. 12.13. A compression joint connecting two lengths of polythene tube

Polythene has not, at the time of writing, being metricated. Because of the thickness of this material it is usually necessary to use a compression fitting one size larger than the nominal size of the equivalent copper tubing. ½in polythene tubing will probably require a 22mm (¾in) fitting. It is however wise to take a sample of the tube along to the supplier to make sure that the right size of fitting is purchased.

Polythene tubing can be bent cold to easy bends but will revert to shape unless firmly secured. Permanent bends may be made by softening the length of pipe by immersion for ten minutes in water that is kept boiling or by *very gently* playing the flame of a blow torch along it.

Unplasticised polyvinyl chloride (u.p.v.c., p.v.c. or vinyl)

Unplasticised polyvinyl chloride is the most versatile of modern plastic materials so far as the plumber is concerned. Pipes of this material may be used for cold water supply, for above and underground drainage and for roof drainage. It is light, tough and easily handled and joined.

P.V.C. cannot be used for hot water under pressure. For this reason there are two, nominally cold water supply pipes which should never be of P.V.C. These are the cold supply pipe from the cold water storage cistern to the hot water cylinder and the cold supply pipe from the feed and expansion system of an indirect hot water system (*Figure 12.14*). Water in these pipes can become very hot at times and, for this reason, metal pipes should always be used.

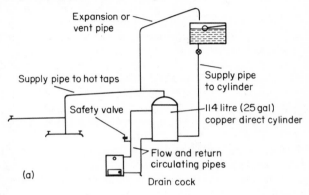

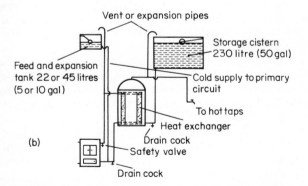

Fig. 12.14. P.V.C. pipes may be used for all cold water pipes except those shown here. (a) A direct hot water system and (b) an indirect hot water system

P.V.C. tubing can be joined either by solvent welding or by ring seal jointing. Solvent welding is always used for cold water supply pipes. For waste and drainage pipes a mixture of the two methods is often used; solvent welding for the small diameter waste pipes and for the connection of junctions and fittings, ring seal jointing for long lengths of the larger diameter stack and drain pipes.

Manufacturers supply fixing instructions which vary slightly with each brand. The following instructions apply to the fixing of Osmflow p.v.c. water supply and distribution pipes.

Cut the pipe to the required length with a hacksaw or other fine toothed saw. Make sure that the pipe end is square and clean off any swarf or burr. With a fine rasp or coarse file chamfer the pipe end to an angle of approximately $15°$.

Roughen the external surface of the pipe end and the internal surface of the socket with a medium grade abrasive paper. Do *not* use steel wool as this will polish the surfaces.

Apply a coat of approved spirit cleaner and degreaser to the inside of the socket and to the pipe end for at least the distance that it will fit into the socket.

Wipe off with clean tissue and apply to both surfaces an even coat of solvent cement. Stroke the cement along, and not round, the surfaces. Thrust pipe end into socket, twist and hold in position for a few seconds. The joint may be handled after two to three minutes but should not be put into operational use for about 24 hours.

Key Terrain Ltd. give similar instructions with their p.v.c. water supply and distribution system but say that the pipe end should *not* be twisted when thrust into the socket. They also suggest that a thicker coat of solvent cement should be applied to the pipe end than to the interior of the socket.

Marley Extrusions Ltd., in their extremely well illustrated instructions for pipework installation, give rather different advice in connection with the solvent welding of their above ground drainage systems (*Figure 12.15*).

The pipe end is cut square, cleaned and degreased in the same way as described earlier but it is not chamfered to an angle. They suggest that, after application of solvent cement to

Half round file

1. Cut the pipe straight and square with a hacksaw. 2. Clean off all swarf and burr inside and out

3. Assemble the fittings and check for length and alignment making pencil mark to ensure accuracy. 4. Apply solvent cement to the outside of the pipe and the inside of the socket, spreading it evenly with a spatula

5
Distribute solvent evenly
with a spatula if necessary,
after application from tube

5. Push the fittings out the end of the pipe with a slight twisting motion until the pipe is fully inserted. 6. Remove surplus cement immediately with a clean dry cloth

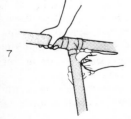

7. Hold the assembled joint in position for about 15 seconds to ensure it stays correctly aligned

Fig. 12.15. Solvent weld jointing of Marley p.v.c. tubing

pipe end and socket interior, the pipe should be thrust into the socket 'with a slight twisting motion' and held in position for about 15 seconds.

A 4m length of p.v.c. pipe will expand by over 13mm when subjected to an increase in temperature of 39°C. For this reason, where a total straight length of waste pipe exceeds 1.8m in length, an expansion coupling should be introduced at 1.8m intervals. The Marley expansion coupling (*Figure 12.16*) has a solvent weld connection at one end and a ring

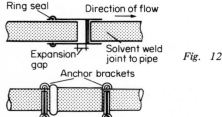

Fig. 12.16. Marley expansion joint

seal joint at the other. An insertion mark made 57mm from the pipe end ensures that accommodation for expansion is provided.

An advantage of ring seal jointing is the facility that it provides for the accommodation of thermal movement due to the passage of hot and cold water through waste and drain pipes. Preparation for ring seal jointing is similar to that for solvent welding (*Figure 12.17*). A fine toothed saw or hacksaw must be used to cut the pipe end absolutely square. Draw a line round the cut end of the pipe 10mm from the end and chamfer back to this line with a rasp or special shaping tool. Insert the pipe into the socket and mark the insertion depth with a pencil. Make another mark 10mm nearer to the pipe end than the first mark. It is to this second mark that the pipe end will finally be inserted, thus leaving 10mm for expansion.

Clean the recess within the pipe socket and insert the sealing ring. Lubricate the pipe end with a small amount of petroleum jelly and push the end firmly home into the socket past the joint ring. Adjust the pipe position so that the insertion depth mark is level with the edge of the socket.

Manufacturers provide a variety of means by which p.v.c. water, waste and drain pipes may be connected to taps and ball-valves, copper or galvanised steel tubing and to stoneware and iron drainage systems.

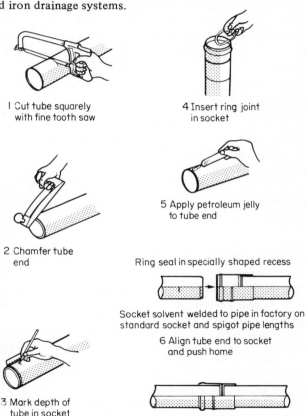

I Cut tube squarely with fine tooth saw

2 Chamfer tube end

3 Mark depth of tube in socket

4 Insert ring joint in socket

5 Apply petroleum jelly to tube end

Ring seal in specially shaped recess

Socket solvent welded to pipe in factory on standard socket and spigot pipe lengths

6 Align tube end to socket and push home

7 Completed joint

Fig. 12.17. Ring seal jointing of p.v.c. pipework

Polypropylene tubing

Polypropylene tubing resembles p.v.c. in many respects. It may be encountered in domestic drainage work but is of greatest value for the drainage of high temperature and chemical wastes from industrial and commercial premises.

The important point of difference between polypropylene and p.v.c. is the fact that the former cannot be joined by solvent welding. Ring seal joints must be used in all situations.

Expanded polystyrene

Expanded polystyrene is used in plumbing as an extremely valuable lagging material. It is obtainable in pipe lagging units which can be fitted round pipes during or subsequent to installation. Tank lagging sets for cold water storage cisterns are also available. Despite its 'porous' appearance it does not, in fact absorb water in any appreciable amount. It can therefore be used to protect underground pipes when required.

Fire risk should always be borne in mind when expanded polystyrene is used. It can burn, giving off dense and potentially lethal fumes.

Pitch fibre pipes

Pitch fibre pipes are sometimes used for above-ground waste and soil stacks. Their most common use however is for underground drainage work.

The simplest method of jointing is undoubtedly the snap ring joint. The snap ring is placed over the end of the pipe, care being taken to ensure that the ring is square to the axis of the pipe and that its flat surface is in contact with the pipe. The coupling is then pushed home over the ring and pipe end so as to force the ring to roll along the pipe (*Figure 12.18*). Due to the shape of the ring's section it is compressed and jumps into its final position. This can be distinctly felt and is an indication of a sound joint.

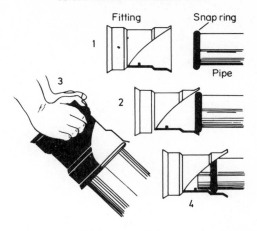

*Fig. 12.18. Making a snap ring joint to pitch
fibre drain pipe*

Pitch fibre pipe can be cut with an ordinary wood saw. Keeping the blade lubricated with water will prevent clogging and speed the operation. As with p.v.c. waste and drain pipes a variety of means are provided for the connection of pitch fibre pipes to pipes and fittings of other materials.

Index